ANIMALS

ANIMALS

igloo

igloo

First published in 2010
by Igloo Books Ltd
Cottage Farm
Sywell
NN6 0BJ
www.igloo-books.com

ISBN 978-0-85734-415-1

Authors:
Leon Gray
Gerard Cheshire
Chris Mattison

Printed and manufactured in China

CONTENTS

INTRODUCTION

Earth is teeming with animal life. From anteaters and axolotls to worms and wildebeest, all the different animals on Earth have adapted to life in many different habitats, from scorching deserts to the frozen polar wastelands.

Animals come in many different shapes and sizes, but they all share certain characteristics. Like all living things, animals are made up of tiny units called cells. Some animals consist of just a few cells, while others are made up of billions upon billions of cells. The cells that make up an animal's body have different jobs to do. Some cells are designed to contract and relax, thus enabling animals to move. Other cells provide the stimulus for responses, such as movement and memory through tiny electrical impulses that travel through the body.

Most animals can move around, but this is not a defining characteristic of animal life. Some species, especially those that live in the water, remain rooted to the spot and look very much like plants. Plants and certain bacteria are the only living things that can make their own food using the energy from the sun. What defines an animal is the fact that it needs to eat food to stay alive. The word 'animal' derives from the Latin *animalis*, meaning 'having vital breath.' In biological terms, the word refers to all members of the kingdom Animalia and it includes organisms ranging from invertebrates to human beings.

Food for fuel

Animals get all the energy they need from food. Food is broken up into simple substances, which are absorbed into the animal's body. These substances are carried to all the cells in the animal's body, where they combine with oxygen to release energy and drive all the different processes inside the cell. The cell then gets rid of any waste products.

Different animals eat different foods. Some are herbivores, which means they eat plants, while others are carnivores that eat other animals. Still others are omnivores, which means they eat both plant and animal food. Parasites live on, or inside the bodies of other animals, while scavengers feed on waste, such as the remains of dead animals and plants. All these different animals are linked by food chains through which energy passes from one species to another.

A world of animals

There are around two million animals living on Earth and many more are waiting to be discovered. The animal kingdom contains species as large as the mighty blue whale, which can reach up to 33 m (108 ft) in length. At the other end of the scale are the countless different microscopic animals, such as gastrotrichs and rotifers, which are just a fraction of a millimeter across.

Most of the larger species in the animal kingdom are vertebrates. Vertebrates have an internal skeleton made up of bone, which supports their large bodies. There are five main groups of vertebrates: fish, amphibians, reptiles, birds and mammals. All the different vertebrates are related to each other, sharing common ancestors that lived millions of years ago. But vertebrates make up only 3 per cent of all the species in the animal kingdom. The remaining 97 per cent is made up of invertebrates, or animals without backbones. Invertebrates include some very large species, such as the giant squid, which can reach more than 13 m (43 ft) long. However, most species are very small and they live in some of the world's most inhospitable environments.

▶ *Uluguru forest tree frog rests on a leaf.*

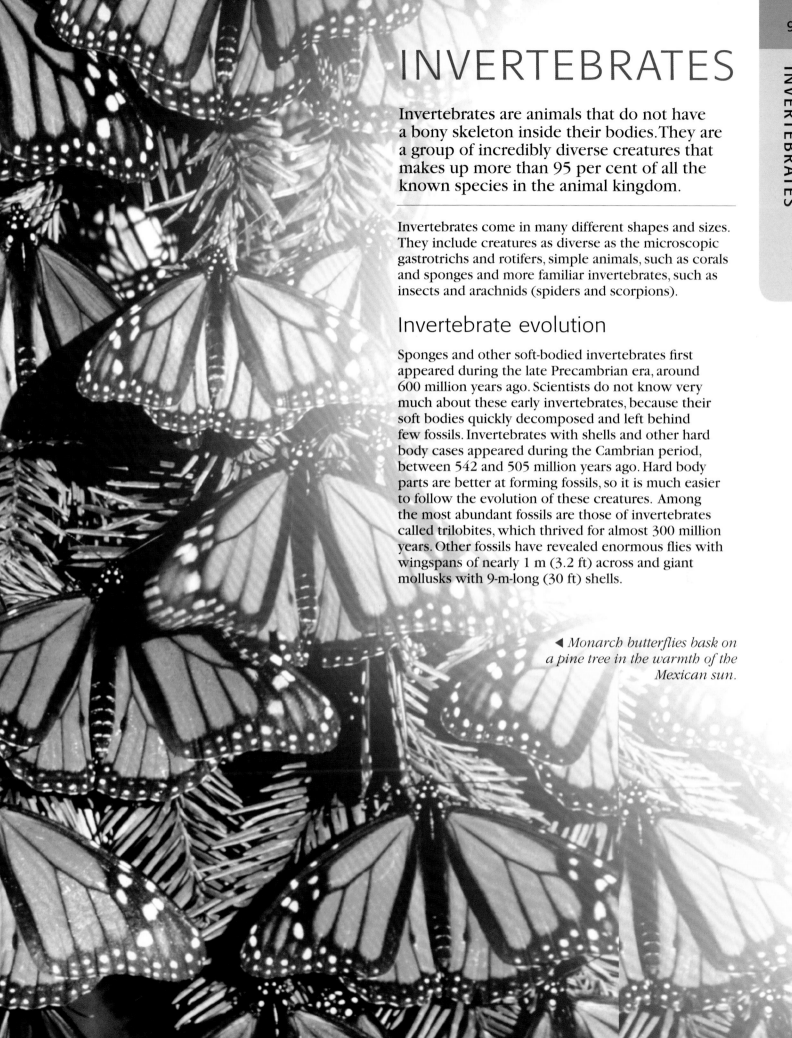

INVERTEBRATES

Invertebrates are animals that do not have a bony skeleton inside their bodies. They are a group of incredibly diverse creatures that makes up more than 95 per cent of all the known species in the animal kingdom.

Invertebrates come in many different shapes and sizes. They include creatures as diverse as the microscopic gastrotrichs and rotifers, simple animals, such as corals and sponges and more familiar invertebrates, such as insects and arachnids (spiders and scorpions).

Invertebrate evolution

Sponges and other soft-bodied invertebrates first appeared during the late Precambrian era, around 600 million years ago. Scientists do not know very much about these early invertebrates, because their soft bodies quickly decomposed and left behind few fossils. Invertebrates with shells and other hard body cases appeared during the Cambrian period, between 542 and 505 million years ago. Hard body parts are better at forming fossils, so it is much easier to follow the evolution of these creatures. Among the most abundant fossils are those of invertebrates called trilobites, which thrived for almost 300 million years. Other fossils have revealed enormous flies with wingspans of nearly 1 m (3.2 ft) across and giant mollusks with 9-m-long (30 ft) shells.

◀ *Monarch butterflies bask on a pine tree in the warmth of the Mexican sun.*

Invertebrate groups

Scientists estimate that there are around five million different invertebrates, but there could be many more because many species have not yet been identified.

The largest and most successful group is the arthropods, which includes the insects, arachnids and crustaceans, such as crabs and lobsters. Scientists think there are more than one million species of arthropods. All of them have a hard outer body case, called an exoskeleton, which is divided into sections. Arthropods also have jointed legs, which are arranged in pairs.

▼ *An octopus darts across the sandy ocean floor. This invertebrate swims backwards.*

Mollusks include invertebrates that usually live inside a shell, for example snails and bivalve mollusks such as clams and mussels. This group of more than 100,000 species also includes the cephalopods – cuttlefish, octopuses and squid. Octopuses do not have a shell, but they have well-developed eyes and are considered to be one of the most intelligent of all invertebrates.

There are three main groups of worms, which account for nearly one million invertebrate species. Segmented worms, or annelids, include the familiar garden earthworms and bloodsucking leeches. Roundworms, or nematodes, are some of the most abundant animals on Earth. As their name suggests, flatworms have flat, ribbon-like bodies. Most flatworms are parasites and live inside the bodies of plants or other animals.

Corals, hydras and jellyfish form another group of aquatic invertebrates called cnidarians. All of these creatures have soft bodies and use stinging cells, called cnidocytes, to immobilize their prey.

Echinoderms are a diverse group of soft-bodied invertebrates that includes familiar creatures, such as starfish and sea urchins, as well as more unusual examples, such as sea cucumbers and feather stars. Almost all echinoderms live on the ocean floor. Most species creep around very slowly to search for food, while others remain rooted to the spot, trapping food using long, feathery tentacles.

While they might seem like plants, sponges are very simple invertebrates. These creatures live on the ocean floor, where they remain fixed to rocks and other hard surfaces. These animals feed on tiny particles of food that pass by in the water current.

Invertebrate reproduction

One of the main reasons for the success of the invertebrates is their ability to reproduce in many different ways. Some invertebrates, such as sponges and starfish, reproduce when parts of the body break off and develop into new individuals. Some insects, such as aphids, develop from eggs that have not been fertilized. The young hatch and develop as clones of their parents. Many invertebrates start their lives as completely different forms to the adults. The eggs hatch as larvae, which grow and develop until the time is right to change into the adult form. This transformation is called metamorphosis and it can happen very suddenly, for example when a caterpillar transforms into a butterfly. In other cases, when the young resemble the adults, the transformation is much more gradual.

▲ *A column of termites carries soil and small stones up a tree to their nest, deep in the rainforest of Borneo, Indonesia.*

▶ *A finger soft coral pokes out from behind an encrusting sponge off the Spanish Costa Brava.*

CENTIPEDES AND MILLIPEDES

Centipedes and millipedes belong to a large group of invertebrates called arthropods, which includes the vast group of the insects as well as crustaceans, such as crabs and arachnids, such as spiders and scorpions.

Centipedes and millipedes are easy to identify. The bodies of these ground-dwelling arthropods are divided into segments. Centipedes have one pair of legs attached to each segment, while millipedes have two pairs. The common names of the centipede and millipede come from the Latin prefixes *centi* (meaning 'hundred') and *milli* (meaning 'thousand') and the Latin *pes* (meaning 'foot'). However, these names are misleading. Centipedes can have anywhere between 20 and more than 300 legs, while millipedes have far fewer legs than their name suggests, usually between 36 and 400.

Despite the similarities in appearance, centipedes and millipedes have evolved to become very different animals. Centipedes are fast-moving, lightweight predators, while millipedes are much slower. They are protected by a thick exoskeleton and usually eat plants or the decomposing remains of other animals.

▼ *A centipede forages in the leaf litter in the rainforest of Sumatra in Indonesia.*

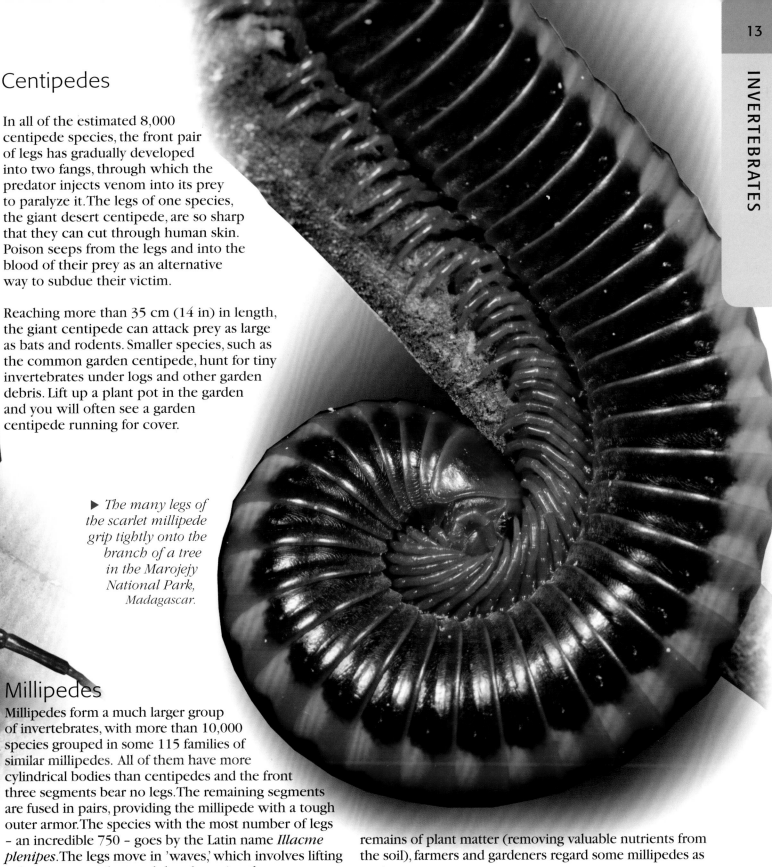

▶ *The many legs of the scarlet millipede grip tightly onto the branch of a tree in the Marojejy National Park, Madagascar.*

Centipedes

In all of the estimated 8,000 centipede species, the front pair of legs has gradually developed into two fangs, through which the predator injects venom into its prey to paralyze it. The legs of one species, the giant desert centipede, are so sharp that they can cut through human skin. Poison seeps from the legs and into the blood of their prey as an alternative way to subdue their victim.

Reaching more than 35 cm (14 in) in length, the giant centipede can attack prey as large as bats and rodents. Smaller species, such as the common garden centipede, hunt for tiny invertebrates under logs and other garden debris. Lift up a plant pot in the garden and you will often see a garden centipede running for cover.

Millipedes

Millipedes form a much larger group of invertebrates, with more than 10,000 species grouped in some 115 families of similar millipedes. All of them have more cylindrical bodies than centipedes and the front three segments bear no legs. The remaining segments are fused in pairs, providing the millipede with a tough outer armor. The species with the most number of legs – an incredible 750 – goes by the Latin name *Illacme plenipes.* The legs move in 'waves,' which involves lifting a dozen or more legs and then lowering them to move the millipede forward.

Most millipedes are herbivores. They eat leaves and other plant matter, secreting juices over the food and then using their jaws to scrape the material into their mouths. Since they eat crops and seedlings and the rotting remains of plant matter (removing valuable nutrients from the soil), farmers and gardeners regard some millipedes as pests.

One unusual millipede, the flat-backed millipede from North America, has bright yellow patches on the body to warn predators of its chemical defense – highly toxic hydrogen cyanide, which seeps through pores in the arthropod's body.

CORALS AND RELATIVES

◄ Coral reefs support the highest biodiversity of any of Earth's ecosystems.

Corals and their relatives belong to a large group called the cnidarians. Jellyfish, sea anemones and hydra-like animals called hydrozoans also belong to this diverse group of mostly marine invertebrates, which includes more than 9,000 species. Hydras are a group of very simple aquatic animals that are related to corals, sea anemones and jellyfish. They are usually just a few millimeters in length and are best studied under a microscope.

What unites this disparate group are the special cells, called cnidocytes, that these animals use to capture their prey. Cnidarians are either sessile (non-moving) organisms, known as polyps, or free-swimming medusae, which are comprised of a mouth surrounded by a ring of tentacles that bear the cnidocytes. They use these stinging cells to trap a wide range of prey, from microscopic plankton to small fish. Cnidarians are prey to a similarly wide range of predators, from starfish and sea slugs to reef fish and turtles.

There are four main groups of cnidarians: the Anthozoa (which includes corals, sea anemones and sea pens), the Scyphozoa (jellyfish), the Cubozoa (box jellyfish) and the Hydrozoa (*Hydra* and relatives such as the infamous Portuguese man-of-war). The classification of the group is open to debate, however, and many biologists recognize separate groups, such as the Staurozoa (stalked jellyfish).

Evolutionary history

Cnidarians have been around for millions of years. The oldest fossils date back to more than 580 million years ago, during a period in Earth's history called the Precambrian era. Experts think that corals first appeared around 490 million years ago. Current thinking suggests that they developed from calcareous sponges from the group Calcarea, although they are also linked to comb jellies (called thus because they are covered with 'combs' of hair-like projections called cilia that beat synchronously and help the animals swim) from the group Ctenophora. What distinguishes them from most other animals is the fact that they are radially symmetrical, which means they have a top and bottom, but no front and back.

Corals

Corals are exclusively marine animals that live in colonies of small, identical units called polyps. The coral you can see develops from one polyp, which divides again and again to form the colony and the visible coral. Corals come in two main types: hard and soft. Hard corals are made up of a hard limestone skeleton, which they use to build up enormous reefs in tropical waters, such as the Great Barrier Reef off the coast of northeastern Australia. Reef-building corals reproduce in a process called 'broadcast spawning,' when all the coral polyps in a reef simultaneously release eggs and sperm into the water. Zoologists have noticed that the time when corals spawn broadly coincides with the time of the full moon. No one really knows why this happens, but it may have something to do with the tides or light conditions.

Soft corals are more plant-like in appearance and lack the limestone skeleton of hard corals. Each soft coral polyp has eight tentacles (as opposed to the 12 tentacles of hard corals) that surround the human mouth and the colonies form an amazing range of different shapes and sizes. For example, the polyps of the grooved brain coral form a wrinkled mass that resembles the human brain.

Jellyfish

Around 300 species of jellyfish form a group of similarly simple invertebrates that drift along in ocean currents in search of food. The main body, or bell, of these animals consists of a mass of jelly-like material that surrounds the opening into the gut. They use their stinging tentacles to paralyze prey and draw it into the gut. Any undigested food passes back out through the same opening.

Jellyfish have developed a rather novel way of getting around – jet propulsion. When a jellyfish wants to move, it relaxes the opening into the gut and fills with water. When the body is full, muscles in the bell contract and push the water through the opening to the gut. The energy of the water jet then pushes the jellyfish forward in the opposite direction.

▼ *Moon jellyfish drift off the coast of Japan, with their stinging tentacles trailing behind them.*

Danger in the sea

Every year, many people swim or surf in the ocean and are stung by jellyfish. The stings of box jellies are particularly dangerous. The tentacles often stick to the skin and the stinging cells pump venom into the body, causing excruciating pain. The best treatment for jellyfish stings is to apply vinegar. This disables any remaining stinging cells in the tentacles, although it does not relieve the initial pain.

Sea anemones

Sea anemones are often called 'sea flowers' because they resemble tiny plants on the rocks of tidal pools or shallow waters. Indeed, these exclusively marine invertebrates are named after anemones – a group of around 120 species of flowering plants.

Like plants, sea anemones do not move too much. Instead, the sea anemone uses its sticky foot to anchor its soft body onto a rock or other hard surface. The cylindrical body opens up into a central disk, or mouth, which is surrounded by stinging tentacles. Stinging cells in the tentacles shoot out when passing prey touches the trigger hair. The cells inject venom into the unfortunate victim and the immobilized victim is then drawn into the mouth. Some animals, notably the clownfish, have developed immunity to the anemone's stinging tentacles. Clownfish make their homes in the tentacles, protected by slimy mucus that covers their bodies.

▼ *Pink tentacles surround the mouth of the fish-eating sea anemone. The tentacles contain the stinging cells that subdue the anemone's prey.*

Other cnidarians

The other main group of cnidarians is the hydrozoans, which include the infamous Portuguese man-of-war and the freshwater *Hydra*. Almost all hydrozoans have two main stages in their life cycle: the hydroid and medusoid stages. The hydroid stage is the typical phase, when individual polyps gather together in colonies to feed. The medusoid stage is the reproductive phase, when the hydrozoans spawn and form new individuals.

Like all cnidarians, hydrozoans use their stinging tentacles to disable their prey. Larger hydrozoans resemble jellyfish and drift along in the ocean currents. The stinging tentacles trail below the surface of the water – occasionally to depths of more than 50 m (164 ft) – where they trap prey, such as small fish and crustaceans. The Portuguese man-of-war is one example. This hydrozoan stings more than 10,000 people every year off the coast of Australia. What makes the Portuguese man-of-war even more dangerous is the fact that the stinging tentacles remain active even if the hydrozoan is dead, or the tentacles are detached. Stings rarely cause death, but the pain is agonizing.

CRUSTACEANS

Crustaceans, such as crabs, lobsters and
shrimps are members of the arthropods,
which include the insects, spiders and
scorpions and centipedes and millipedes.
Almost all crustaceans are aquatic animals and
have two pairs of antennae, a pair of eyes and
a body covered with tough body armor, called
an exoskeleton.

The ancestors of modern crustaceans are well
documented in the fossil record and date back to at
least the Cambrian period, some 545 million years ago.
Indeed, some of today's crustaceans have changed
so little that they are regarded as living fossils. The
horseshoe shrimp is one example, having retained the
same basic body shape since it first emerged in the
Triassic period, between 248 and 208 million years ago.

Basic body shape

All crustaceans share certain key features. The body
is usually divided into three distinct segments – head,
thorax and abdomen – although the head and thorax
may be fused to form a cephalothorax. The head has
two compound eyes on eyestalks and two pairs of
antennae. The body is covered with a hard exoskeleton,
strengthened with a compound called calcium
carbonate. The shell is shed periodically to allow the
crustacean to grow. The thorax and abdomen bear pairs
of limbs that may be used for walking or feeding, but
the exact number varies between the different groups
of crustaceans. This variety may be one factor that has
contributed to the success of the group.

◄ *The Christmas Island red
crab seen during its annual
migration across the island.*

Different groups

Crustaceans form a large and very diverse group of arthropods. Experts think that there are at least 50,000 different crustacean species, but the real figure could be much higher. These largely aquatic invertebrates range in size from the almost microscopic copepods right up to the heavily armored Japanese spider crab, which weighs up to 20 kg (44 lb) and has a leg span of more than 4 m (13 ft).

There are six main groups of crustaceans. The most familiar groups include the branchiopods, which include species, such as brine shrimp and water fleas, maxillopods, which include the barnacles and copepods and the malacostracans (the largest group) that contains the most familiar crustaceans, such as crabs, lobsters and shrimp, as well as all the ground-living species, such as woodlice.

While most species are free-living aquatic animals, some species, such as barnacles, are sessile and live attached to rocks. Others, such as fish lice and mouth worms, are parasites and live on the bodies of other animals. Still others, such as woodlice, have even ventured onto the land.

▲ *Woodlice gather under the bark of a dead elm tree.*

Crustacean reproduction

Most crustaceans reproduce sexually, which means that males release sperm cells to fertilize the female egg cells. Once the male and female have paired up, the fertilized eggs are usually left to drift away. The females of some species hold on to the eggs, however, keeping them in special brood pouches, or fixed onto long sticky threads. The eggs then hatch into larvae, which go through several stages of development before they start to resemble the adults.

A few crustaceans do not reproduce sexually. Some, such as barnacles, are hermaphrodites, which means they possess both male and female reproductive organs and can fertilize themselves. Others reproduce by a process called parthenogenesis, when the females produce eggs that hatch into new crustaceans without being fertilized by male sperm. A few simple crustaceans, such as water fleas, exhibit this unusual reproductive behavior, as do some 'higher' species, such as the Marmorkrebs crayfish.

Crustaceans in the food chain

Many crustaceans are a very important part of the food chain. Microscopic krill and copepods are food for many marine animals, while more familiar crustaceans, such as crabs, lobsters, prawns and shrimp are popular human food. In 2007, more than 11 million tons of these crustaceans were either taken from the sea or raised in purpose-built fisheries. Demand is particularly high in Asia, with China responsible for nearly half the world's supply.

Help or hindrance

While many crustaceans live a free-swimming lifestyle, others choose to hitch a ride and live on other animals. This is known as parasitism and it is practiced by crustaceans such as sea lice, which cling to the skin of fish and tongue worms, which fix on to the bodies of their hosts and tap into their blood supply. Parasitism is an unhealthy relationship since it only benefits the parasite and often harms the host. Other crustaceans have developed relationships with other species, in which both animals benefit. For example, Pacific cleaner shrimp gather in cleaning stations on coral reefs and remove parasites and dead tissue from different fish, some of which are dangerous predators. The shrimp get a free meal and protection from other predators for their services, while the host fish get cleaned.

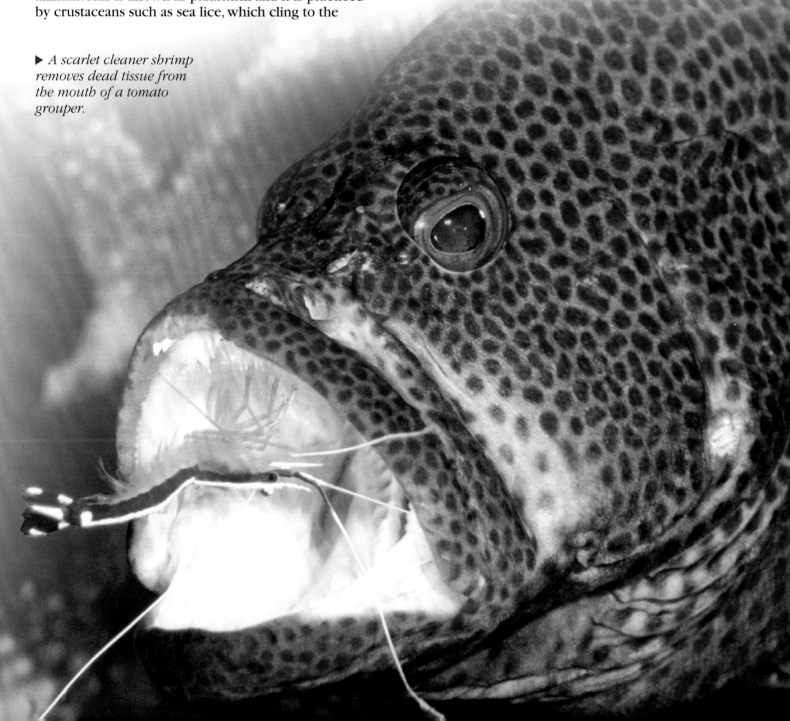

▶ *A scarlet cleaner shrimp removes dead tissue from the mouth of a tomato grouper.*

Compound eye

Head

Thorax

Wing pair

Abdomen

▼ *The broad-bodied chaser has a typical insect body plan, with a distinct head, thorax and abdomen. The chaser has two pairs of wings attached to the thorax; other insects have only one wing pair.*

INSECTS

Insects are some of the most successful and adaptable animals on our planet. They are part of the large group of the arthropods, which make up more than 80 per cent of all known animals. They are related to spiders and scorpions, centipedes and millipedes and crustaceans, such as crabs and lobsters.

Insects are incredible animals. Imagine you could lift 50 times your own body weight – that's the equivalent of an average adult lifting a truck. Ants do this all the time as they carry crumbs of food, grains of dirt and sand and pebbles back to their colony. Most fleas are just a few millimeters long, but they can jump up to 18 cm (7 in) – that's the equivalent of an average human jumping the length of three football pitches!

▲ *This fossilized trilobite dates back to the Ordovician period, between 490 and 443 million years ago.*

Insect evolution

Fossils suggest that the first insects appeared about 440 million years ago, during a period in Earth's history called the Silurian period. The earliest insects developed from other primitive invertebrates that included marine arthropods called trilobites, which were one of the dominant marine life forms during the Cambrian period (around 542 to 488 million years ago).

The first true insects probably developed from the terrestrial descendants of trilobites – millipede-like creatures that lacked wings. Winged insects appeared during the Devonian period about 70 million years later. Their wings stuck out at right angles to the body and flapped up and down to provide the lift force. These early winged insects are the Paleoptera, or 'old wings' and they are the ancestors of modern-day mayflies and dragonflies. Being able to fly offered these early insects huge advantages over other animals and they evolved into many different groups very quickly. These winged insects were extremely successful during the Carboniferous period (between 359 and 299 million years ago), when some grew into huge and fearsome predators. By the end of the Permian period (between 299 and 251 million years ago), most of the modern insect groups had appeared and were spreading out to occupy almost every habitat on Earth.

Insect anatomy

All insects have the same basic body plan, with three pairs of legs and three main body parts – the head, thorax and abdomen. The head bears appendages called antennae, which the insect uses to feel its way around, mouthparts and simple or compound eyes. The thorax is the middle section of an insect's body and can be divided into three sections called metameres. Each metamere bears a pair of legs, to make up the six legs that all insects have. Small openings, called spiracles, are present on the thorax and these extend to the abdomen. Spiracles are connected to the insect's respiratory system and allow insects to breathe. The body of an insect is covered with a tough outer coat, called an exoskeleton, which is made of a substance called chitin – the same substance that makes up our own fingernails and hair. The exoskeleton acts like the internal skeleton of vertebrate animals, providing a framework for the muscles and protection for the insect's internal organs. The exoskeleton also offers some protection from predators.

Most insects have one or two pairs of wings; even those insects that do not appear to have wings have small, vestigial wings on the thorax. Wings give insects a considerable advantage over other animals. They enable insects to escape from predators on the ground and move away when the population expands and it becomes too crowded. Wings also enabled insects to spread out and inhabit some of the most inhospitable places on Earth.

Reproduction and development

Wings are not the only reason why insects have become some of the most successful animals. They have also developed a unique range of breeding behaviors, which has enabled them to reproduce very quickly. All insects reproduce by laying eggs, which can be deposited in large clusters or as a single egg. Insects can reproduce sexually, when a male sperm cell fertilizes the female egg cell, but they can also reproduce asexually from eggs that have not been fertilized by a male. This form of reproduction, called parthenogenesis, is common among insects such as aphids and cockroaches.

When the eggs hatch, the young of some insects may resemble miniature version of the adults. The young (called nymphs) then shed their exoskeleton (molt) periodically – usually between four and eight times – until they have grown to their adult size. By this time, they will have grown their wings. This is known as incomplete metamorphosis and only a few insects, such as locusts, reproduce in this way.

Most insects reproduce in a process called complete metamorphosis. When the eggs hatch, the young do not resemble the adult insects at all. These young, called larvae, have a wormlike appearance. Some larvae live and feed on plants, sucking the sap from the plant's juicy stems and fruits. Others live on animals and feed on their host, or they may live in water and eat smaller animals.

Eventually, the larvae reach a point where they must pupate. Some larvae build a cocoon of woven fibres or saliva around their bodies, while others bury themselves in a hole in the ground. Most spend the winter in this state, and then emerge the following spring as the fully formed adult.

◀ *The adult rhinoceros beetle can lift more than 850 times its own body weight, making it one of the strongest animals on the planet.*

▲ *Honeybees gather pollen on their hind legs and bring it back to the hive.*

Insect groups

No one knows for sure how many different types of insects there are. Entomologists (scientists who specialize in studying insects) have identified around one million different species and they are finding new ones every day. In fact, the insects include the largest number of species of any group of animals, and they have spread out to live in almost every area, from barren deserts to coastal marine or saline habitats.

Ants and termites are social insects that live in large colonies throughout the world. In most colonies, a huge army of worker ants serve one breeding female, called the queen. The workers build and defend the nests and find food for the larvae. Termites also live in large colonies and often build huge mounds that tower over the landscape. These nests protect the termites from predators such as lizards. Termites often munch their way through valuable crops, so they are considered as pests in many countries.

Bees and wasps are typical flying insects with two pairs of wings and large compound eyes. Many live in large colonies, though some prefer a solitary existence. The main difference between bees and wasps are the feeding habits – most wasps are predators and eat other insects, while bees feed on the pollen and nectar of plants. Honeybees are very important as a source of honey. People raise colonies of honeybees to collect the honey. This is known as apiculture (beekeeping) and has been practiced since the time of the ancient Egyptians.

Beetles and bugs are two very different groups of insects. Many people use the word 'bug' to describe many different types of insects, but to entomologists bugs are members of a particular group, the Hemiptera. Bugs are a diverse group, but they all feed by stabbing their sharp beaks into animals or plants and sucking up the fluids. Beetles are the biggest group of insects, ranging in size from the aptly named Hercules beetle at more than 19 cm (7.5 in) in length, to the tiny *Nanosella* beetles, which measure just a few hundred micrometers (millionths of a meter) in length. Beetles are some of the most successful insects and have spread all over the world. Their wings are held under protective wing cases called elytra.

◀ *An army ant living on Barro Colorado Island, Panama, carries food back to its colony.*

Butterflies and moths form a large group of around 170,000 species. Butterflies are some of the most striking insects, with bright wings covered in colorful scales. However, most of the members of this group are the moths, which are usually active at night. Butterflies and moths both develop through complete metamorphosis. The larvae are known as caterpillars, which are feeding machines that munch their way through vast quantities of leaves. Eventually, the caterpillars stop eating and build a cocoon around their bodies. Inside, the caterpillar changes into the adult butterfly or moth, which then breaks out of the cocoon and flies away.

Cockroaches and mantises are a successful group of insects that live throughout the world. Cockroaches are flat, robust insects that rest during the day and come out at night to feed on the rotting remains of plants or dead animals. Cockroaches are familiar pests in many parts of the world, feeding on human food and spreading disease in the process. The mantises are bizarre-looking

relatives of the cockroaches. These fearsome predators hunt during the day, lying in wait for passing prey. The mantis then strikes out with unbelievable speed, catching its prey on spiky forelegs.

Dragonflies and damselflies are almost identical to insects that were flying around almost 300 million years ago. They have long, thin bodies and two pairs of large wings. The wings of dragonflies stick out at right angles to the body, while those of damselflies fold along the back. These amazing flying insects are formidable predators, zooming around at speeds of up to 30 km (19 mi) per hour and zooming in on their prey with huge compounds eyes. However, dragonflies and damselflies spend most of their lives as larvae, swimming around in the murky depths of freshwater lakes and ponds.

▼ *A blue morpho butterfly (Morpho peleides) rests on a leaf. The bright blue color of this butterfly is a result of the diffraction of light from the scales of its wings.*

Classification

Insect classification is constantly changing as entomologists identify more species. Scientists classify insects into groups, or orders, of related species. Such orders include:

Coleoptera	Beetles
Collembola	Springtails
Dermaptera	Earwigs
Dictyoptera	Cockroaches and mantises
Diplura	Two-pronged bristletails
Diptera	True flies, gnats and mosquitoes
Embioptera	Webspinners
Ephemeroptera	Mayflies
Hemiptera	True bugs
Hymenoptera	Ants, bees and wasps
Isoptera	Termites
Lepidoptera	Butterflies and moths
Mallophaga	Biting lice
Mecoptera	Scorpionflies
Megaloptera	Alderflies
Neuroptera	Lacewings
Odonata	Dragonflies and damselflies
Orthoptera	Crickets, grasshoppers and locusts
Phasmida	Stick and leaf insects
Plecoptera	Stoneflies
Psocoptera	Booklice
Rhaphidioptera	Snakeflies
Siphonaptera	Fleas
Siphunculata	Sucking lice
Strepsiptera	Stylopids
Thysanoptera	Thrips (thunderflies)
Thysanura	Bristletails and silverfish
Trichoptera	Caddis flies
Zoraptera	Tropical insects that live in rotting timber and sawdust

▲ *A European mantis lies in wait, ready to snap up its next meal.*

Crickets, grasshoppers and locusts are a large group of insects that contains up to 20,000 species. All have long, powerful hind legs, which they use to jump away from predators. These insects are famous for their chirping "song," which fills the air during the breeding season. Grasshoppers communicate by rubbing their legs against their wings to produce the chirping song, while crickets rub their wings together. All of the members of this group develop through incomplete metamorphosis.

Flies and mosquitoes are another large group of insects that usually have just a single pair of wings, large compound eyes and either sharp mouthparts to pierce through tough food or fleshy feeding tubes to suck up food. Flies eat a wide variety of food, ranging from rotting plants and plant nectar to animal dung and human sweat. This group contains one of the deadliest animals on the planet – the mosquito. This tiny insect is responsible for spreading the disease malaria, which kills millions of people every year.

Leaf and stick insects are the kings and queens of camouflage, blending seamlessly into the plants on which they live. Most species live in the dense forest of tropical regions, but they are found around the world thanks to their popularity as pets. As their names suggest, leaf insects look like leaves, with dull green and brown bodies and spots and blotches that look like the blemishes on real leaves. Stick insects have slender brown and green bodies that resemble green shoots and twigs.

MICROSCOPIC ANIMALS

Most animals are made up of many cells, but some are so small that they cannot be seen by the naked eye. These microscopic animals form a diverse group of incredibly small living things, ranging from the filter-feeding rotifers to the wormlike gastrotrichs.

Microscopic animals generally measure less than 1 mm (0.04 in) in length. Many are found in freshwater habitats and the open ocean, where they usually live on submerged surfaces, such as rocks, or the bodies of other marine organisms. Others live buried in the sediment of the seabed, while others occupy the depths of the ocean, where very little else can survive. Not all microscopic animals live in water – they can thrive anywhere, from the soil in your garden to the pillows on your bed.

Different groups

Microscopic animals come from a range of different animal groups. There are numerous microscopic crustaceans, such as copepods and cladocerans. Copepods are found in almost every aquatic environment on Earth. Most species drift in the open ocean or live on the ocean floor, but some are found in more unusual aquatic environments, such as the water-filled cups of plants, such as bromeliads. Cladocerans are commonly known as water fleas. There are around 400 different species, which are usually found in freshwater habitats. Microscopic worms include planarians

(flatworms) and nematodes (roundworms, hookworms and threadworms). Nematodes are particularly abundant in the ocean, making up nearly 90 per cent of all the different species that live on the ocean floor. Microscopic dust mites are found in every home on the planet. These tiny creatures live on the dead skin cells that continually flake off our bodies. Other microscopic mites live on the leaves of plants, piercing through the surface of the leaf to suck the sap found inside.

Placozoans

These primitive invertebrates have simple flat bodies (the word placozoan means "flat animal") with no clear body tissues or organs. There is only one identified species, but scientists know so little about placozoans that there may be more. One idea is that placozoans are the evolutionary link between animals and non-animal groups, such as the protozoans. Scientists are now studying the DNA of these animals to see if they can prove the hypothesis.

Rotifers

Rotifers are some of the smallest microscopic animals and come in a wide range of shapes and sizes. The smallest rotifers measure around 50 µm (millionths of a meter), but most species are between 0.1 and 0.5 mm (0.004 and 0.02 in) long. Most species have wormlike bodies with a distinct head, trunk and foot. The trunk is the main body of the animal and contains the main organs, while the foot projects from the end of the trunk and looks a little like a tail. The foot may end in between one and four toes, which many species use to crawl around on the surface of submerged rocks.

Rotifers are generally freshwater invertebrates, but a few species live in the open ocean. Most species are free-swimming animals that form part of the freshwater zooplankton – an important source of food for other animals. In turn, rotifers eat a wide variety of waste, ranging from algae to dead bacteria. In this way, rotifers help to keep the aquatic environment clean.

◄ *Rotifers are tiny animals that live in freshwater rivers and lakes, feeding on other microscopic organisms and animal waste.*

Gastrotrichs

Gastrotrichs are another group of tiny, wormlike invertebrates that are usually found in freshwater or the open ocean. There are around 700 species in the group and they all resemble flat, transparent tubes. Close examination under a microscope will reveal anterior and posterior ends. The body is covered with tiny projections, called cilia, which are the sensory organs. Some gastrotrichs also have photosensitive cells as part of a simple nervous system.

Gastrotrichs are hermaphrodites, which means they have both male and female sex organs. Most gastrotrichs reproduce sexually, where

▶ *Dinoflagellates are primitive animals that float in the water column, beating their tiny flagella (tail-like projections) to move around.*

one individual transfers sperm to another individual. In some species, the male sex organs do not play a part in reproduction or may even be absent. In this case, the gastrotrich reproduces asexually and the female produces eggs without fertilization.

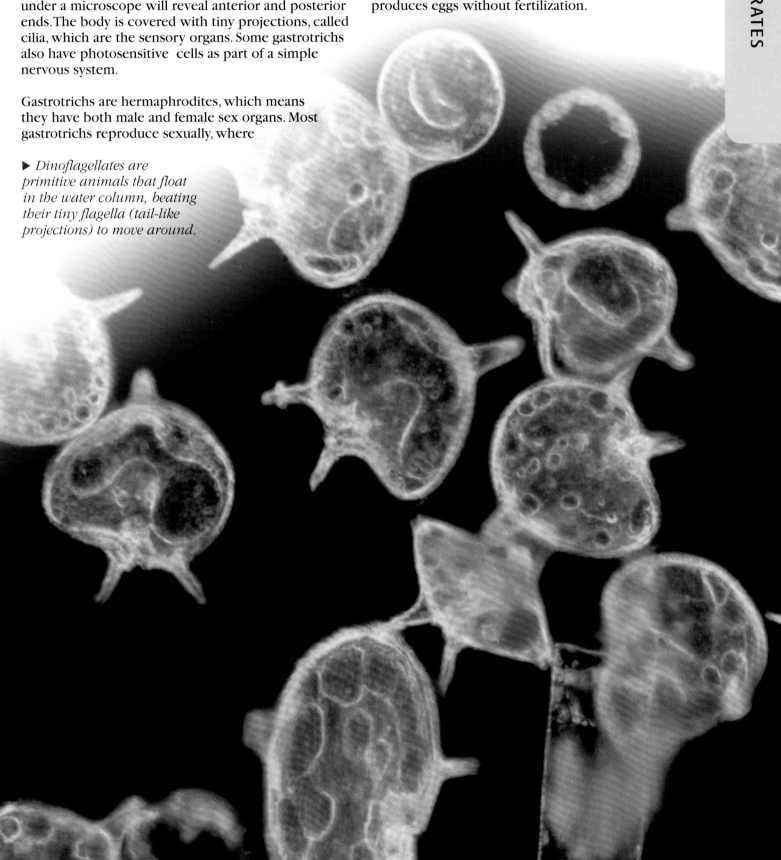

MOLLUSKS

Mollusks are a large and diverse group of invertebrates that come in many different shapes and sizes. They range from tiny snails, which are just a few millimeters across, to the aptly named colossal squid, which can reach up to 15 m (49 ft) long.

Mollusks are one of the largest groups in the animal kingdom, with more than 100,000 living species and 30,000 extinct species. They exhibit a range of different body forms. Some have hard outer shells that enclose their bodies and protect them from attack. Others have soft bodies and produce bitter-tasting chemicals to deter predators. Some mollusks live on the land and slowly creep along the ground using their sucker-like feet. Others live in the oceans and move rapidly, squirting a jet of water through their bodies in an animal form of rocket propulsion.

Common characteristics

All mollusks have some type of shell as part of their bodies. The shell is made up of crystals of a substance called calcium carbonate, which the mollusk secretes from its mantle. The shells show an almost endless variety of colors and forms – even within similar groups of mollusks. The presence of the shell has left a rich fossil record, dating back millions of years in Earth's history.

Another feature common to almost all mollusks is a feeding structure called the radula, which is a sharp ridge that projects out of the mollusk's mouth. The radula grinds down the food particles and draws them into the mouth, where they pass into the mollusk's simple digestive system. One group of mollusks feed in a different way, trapping waterborne particles of food in their gills.

◀ *A garden snail slides on a layer of mucus, using 'eyes' at the tips of its feelers to find its way around.*

▲ *Common mussels cling to the surface of a rock on the coast of Devon in England.*

Mollusk groups

Scientists recognize seven main groups of mollusks. **Monoplacophorans** are a small group of about seven species of deep-sea mollusks that were first discovered in 1952, off the Pacific coast of Costa Rica. These primitive mollusks have simple plate-like shells, five, or more pairs of gills and a poorly developed head. They live in the depths of the ocean, where they feed on plankton and material grazed from the seabed.

Polyplacophorans make up a larger group of around 700 species that range in size from a few centimeters to more than 30 cm (12 in). Also known as chitons, these mollusks have flat bodies, with a shell divided into eight segments. These mollusks use their radula to scrape plant and animal food from rocks and other surfaces on the ocean floor.

Aplacophorans are an unusual group of about 250 mollusks that lack the shell and mantle common to most members of the group but feed using the rasping radula. These wormlike mollusks generally measure up to 5 cm (2 in) long and live on the ocean floor, or among soft corals. They are predators, or scavengers and eat a wide range of plant and animal material.

Scaphopodans are a group of marine mollusks that are enclosed within a curved, tubular shell, which is open at both ends and resembles a tusk (giving these mollusks their common name 'tusk shells'). There are about 350 living species and most are less than 6 cm (2.4 in) across. Most species bury themselves in the sediment, with one end sticking out so water can circulate through the shell. They use small tentacles to gather up and eat small microscopic organisms and drifting plant matter.

Gastropods usually have a single shell, although some species have no shell at all. There are around 75,000 living species and 15,000 extinct species. Gastropods live in a wide range of habitats. Some gastropods are collected as food and are considered a delicacy, while others are vectors for organisms that cause diseases, such as schistosomiasis.

Many gastropods have a complex head, with elaborate receptors and a developed nervous system. Some have developed coiled shells and can withdraw inside the shell to avoid predators. The group includes the familiar terrestrial snails and slugs, as well as shellfish such as limpets and whelks. It also includes sea slugs and their relatives, which have lost their shells but carry another defense – their sting. Many species have dazzling colors to warn predators to stay away. Gastropods show many other interesting adaptations, which have made them some of the most successful of all mollusk species.

Bivalves have shells in two parts and can pull them both together to seal themselves safely inside. There are around 12,000 species and most are found in the oceans, where they can range in size from a few millimeters to more than one meter. Most bivalves have one or two protruding tubes, called siphons, which allow water to flow through the shells. They also have feathery gills, which they use to trap food particles from sediment in the water column.

Many bivalves are extremely important to people as a source of food – examples include mussels, oysters and scallops. Increased demand for these shellfish has led to overharvesting and many bivalves are now farmed.

Bivalves are also the source of pearls, which form when a tiny grain of sand gets inside the shell and causes irritation. In response, the bivalve secretes a substance called nacre (mother-of-pearl), which covers the grain and reduces the irritation.

Cephalopods are the final group of mollusks and include the familiar squid and octopuses. These animals have long tentacles covered with suckers, which they use to grab prey, such as crabs, fish and other mollusks. Squid and cuttlefish have an internal shell, which supports their bodies like the skeleton of a vertebrate. Octopuses do not have a shell. Both have well-developed eyes, which can distinguish shapes and help them to locate and catch prey.

Studies have shown that octopuses are intelligent animals. These mollusks have the largest brains of any invertebrates and a well-developed nervous system. In tests, octopuses have escaped from mazes and shown the ability to learn by copying other octopuses.

Evolution of mollusks

All the different mollusks on Earth developed from ancestors that lived millions of years ago. Fossil evidence suggests that the earliest ancestors of mollusks appeared around 542 million years ago, during a period in Earth's history called the early Cambrian. At this time, most of the world's surface was covered with vast shallow seas teeming with life.

The nautilus is a living fossil, having changed relatively little since its ancestors first appeared during the early Cambrian

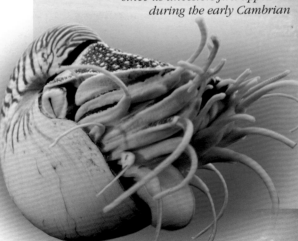

▲ *The sea cucumber (Stichopus variegatus) crawls across the ocean floor in search of food.*

Feeding habits

Echinoderms show a wide range of feeding behaviors. Some starfish are scavengers and feed on almost any kind of dead animal matter. Others are deadly predators and feed on other marine animals, such as corals and sponges. The crown-of-thorns starfish is such a voracious predator of coral that it is partly responsible for the destruction of coral reefs in the Indian and Pacific Oceans.

Predatory starfish can push their stomachs through their mouths to engulf their prey. The starfish then secretes enzymes onto the body of its victim and sucks up the digested juices. Other echinoderms feed in different ways, for example by trapping particles in the water current using long, feathery tentacles.

Echinoderm reproduction

Most echinoderms have separate males and females, which reproduce by casting the sperm and egg cells into the water. To ensure success, the males and females produce vast quantities of sex cells. Fertilized eggs develop into embryos that go through several stages of development before they become the adult echinoderms. Other echinoderms are hermaphroditic, which means they have both male and female sex organs and can reproduce without the need for a mate.

Different echinoderms

Scientists think that there are at least 7,000 different species of echinoderms that are divided into six main groups. Starfish form one large group, which range in size from a few centimeters to more than 1 m (3 ft). All starfish have flat, star-shaped bodies with several arms spreading out from a central disk. Most starfish have five arms, but some species have many more. Brittlestars and basket stars are some of the largest echinoderms. They have long, slender arms that can break off but regrow again. Sea urchins belong to a group of their own. These unusual sea creatures generally live on the sea floor and use their long tentacles to catch food in water currents. Sea lilies and feather stars are another group of echinoderms. These creatures have star-shaped bodies and can be found in the water column, or on the sea floor. Sea cucumbers have fleshy, cucumber-like bodies, ranging in size from a few centimeters to more than 1 m (3 ft). The final group are called sea daisies. These echinoderms are found within a limited range off the coast of New Zealand, in the Bahamas and most recently, the northern central Pacific.

FISH

There are many animals in the world described as fish. Here we discuss only those species that are true fish. Animals that are not true fish but sometimes get confused with fish include starfish, cuttlefish, jellyfish, silverfish and shellfish.

The group of animals known scientifically as fish comprises a very diverse selection of species, ranging from primitive jawless fish to advanced bony and cartilaginous fish. In evolutionary terms, the fish group comes above simple chordates (animals possessing spinal chords), such as sea squirts and lancelets and below amphibians, such as frogs, toads and newts.

There is some degree of argument about the exact classification (taxonomy) of fish types, mainly because the group is so large and contains species from several biological classes. Although these classes are related, the species they contain are often quite different apart from some anatomical details that demonstrate their similarity. This is known as cladistic assimilation.

As all fish live in water, most breathe via gills and most possess a fusiform body, which means they are tapered at both ends to assist in efficient swimming. They also have fins rather than limbs, which they use for propulsion, steering and breaking in their aquatic habitats. Most fish are carnivorous, but some species are omnivorous and a few are herbivorous. They have also adapted to live in freshwater, salt water and brackish water. This means that fish can be found in oceans, seas, rivers, lakes, ponds and even caves. As water accounts for over 90 per cent of the three-dimensional living space of Earth's biosphere, fish have a great deal of environment to exploit. This explains why they make up the majority of vertebrate species on the planet, alongside amphibians, reptiles, birds and mammals.

◀ *Coral reefs are the best places to see a wide variety of fish in one place.*

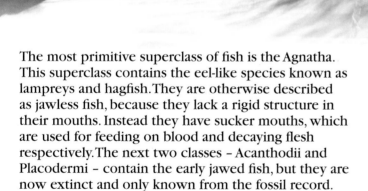

The most primitive superclass of fish is the Agnatha. This superclass contains the eel-like species known as lampreys and hagfish. They are otherwise described as jawless fish, because they lack a rigid structure in their mouths. Instead they have sucker mouths, which are used for feeding on blood and decaying flesh respectively. The next two classes – Acanthodii and Placodermi – contain the early jawed fish, but they are now extinct and only known from the fossil record.

The bony fish superclass Osteichthyes comprises more than 23,000 living species, which are thought of as typical fish. They possess fully developed bony skeletons and most have rigid rays within their fins, making them teleosts, which is derived from the Greek words *teleios*, meaning 'perfect or complete' and *osteon*, meaning 'bone.' The few that are not ray-fins include sturgeons, paddlefish and bowfins. Most bony fish have scales covering their bodies for protection. Lobe-finned fish (subclass Sarcopterygii) include the marine coelacanth, which is described as a living fossil due to its singular survival and the freshwater lungfish.

▲ *A cleaner wrasse is seen cleaning parasites from the gills of a larger fish.*

The cartilaginous fish class Chondrichthyes contains the sharks, skates and rays. It used to be thought that these fish were more primitive than bony fish, but opinion has since swayed in scientific circles, so that cartilage is now viewed as a modification. As well as having skeletons made from cartilage, these fish have dermal teeth covering their bodies instead of scales. Although their skin feels extremely rough to the touch, it is counter-intuitive as it enables them to swim faster through water. As these fish are typically hunters, this evolved detail gives them a survival advantage.

▶ *The whale shark is easily the largest species of true fish, it can reach lengths of 12 m (40 ft), or more, thankfully for most sea creatures its favorite food is plankton.*

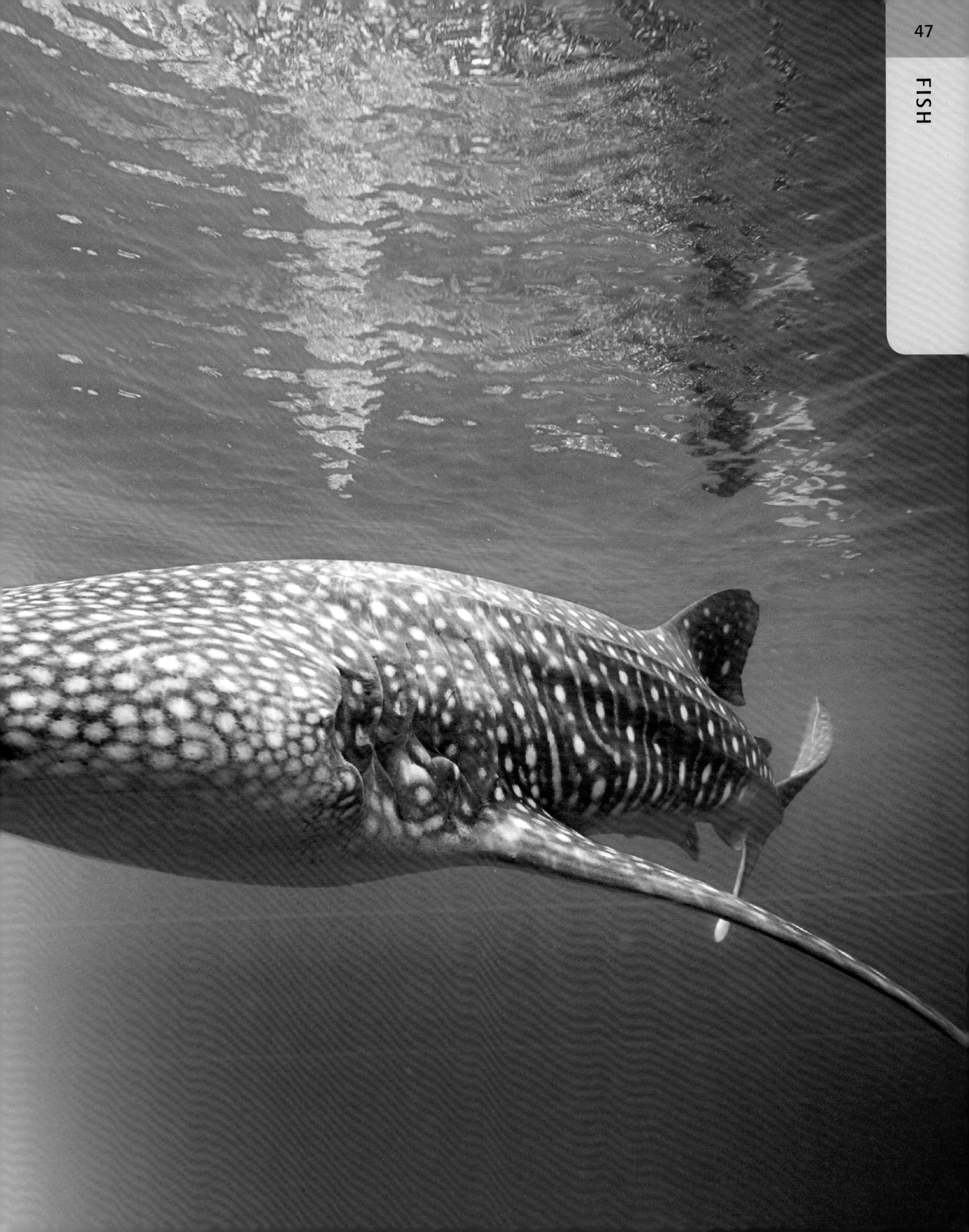

JAWLESS FISH

The first fish to evolve were fairly basic, with spinal chords and only partial skeletons. However, they set the blueprint for vertebrates, so that all later fish, amphibians, reptiles, birds and mammals, including humans, evolved from them.

▲ *The gills of a lamprey are a series of holes through which water passes from the mouth.*

The class of fish Agnatha – the jawless fish – contains the lampreys and the hagfish. Both groups are eel-like in form, although true eels belong to the bony fish superclass. As their common name indicates, these fish do not have structured jaws as other fish do. Instead they have sucker mouths, lined with teeth with which they abrade the surface of their food. In the case of lampreys, they attach themselves to other fish and feed on their blood. In the case of hagfish, the decomposing flesh of other animals is their meal.

Hagfish

There is some disagreement about the classification of hagfish as they happen to be the only chordates that possess skulls but have no vertebral column, making them somewhat more primitive than lampreys. Consequently, they are given their own class Myxini. Hagfish are part of the 'clean-up squad' as they play their part in the decomposition and recycling of dead animal bodies lying on the seabed. They are designed to puncture holes in the skin of dead animals and then drill their way inside, consuming the decomposing flesh as they go. To assist in this way of life, they are able to produce large quantities of slime as lubrication and they are also able to literally tie themselves in knots, which they can then move along their bodies, thereby enabling them to extract themselves from tight holes that generate a vacuum.

The slime may also serve to deter predatory fish, as it gels with water and clogs the mouth and gills, assisting in escape. Hagfish will also attack dying animals, burrowing inside their bodies and finishing them off by devouring their internal organs. Due to the sporadic availability of food, hagfish can survive for months without feeding, but feed keenly when the chance arises.

◄ *The lamprey's mouth is like a suction cup with teeth, for feeding on the blood of other fish.*

Hagfish have barbels around their mouths and simple eyes, but relatively little is known of their sensory equipment and how they detect their food. Similarly, much detail of their reproduction and life cycle awaits scientific investigation. They typically inhabit deep water environments, where behavioral observations are difficult and expensive to conduct. They are known to lay eggs, from which young hagfish hatch, whereas lampreys have a larval stage before adults develop.

Hagfish are so called, because the word 'hag' once denoted ugliness, alluding to both the fish's appearance and habits.

Lampreys

Lampreys are parasitic fish, as they feed on the blood of other living fish. Their mouths are lined with concentric circles of teeth designed to saw their way through the scales of their hosts and then rupture the blood vessels in their skin. The lamprey then gorges itself on blood until it is satisfied and goes on its way. Host fish can die from blood loss, but they are usually much larger than lampreys and are able to recover.

The name lamprey is derived from the Latin *lambere* for 'lick' and *petra* for 'stone,' meaning 'stone licker,' because the fish also use their sucker mouths to hold onto stones in fast flowing rivers, thus enabling them to save on energy when traveling upstream.

SHARK FAMILY

▼ *The fearsome great white shark has a tail powerful enough to thrust it out of the water.*

The fish of the Chondrichthyes class all have skeletons made from cartilage, rather than bone. Cartilage is a flexible material containing collagen, which is also present in bone alongside brittle calcium compounds. Members of the shark family, therefore, have tough and bendable skeletons.

Cartilaginous fish are generally designed by nature to be stealthy predators, usually hunting other fish but also preying on invertebrates, reptiles, birds and mammals when the chance arises. Most species live in marine habitats only, although a few have adapted to cope with brackish water and freshwater.

Giant sharks

The largest shark species is the whale shark (*Rhincodon typus*), which can grow in excess of 12 m (39 ft) and lives in the open ocean. Despite its size, the whale shark is a benign fish as it has adapted to eat plankton by filtering it from seawater. Plankton can comprise all manner of small organisms in adult or larval form. The term zooplankton describes plankton consisting of animal species, while phytoplankton is the term used for plankton consisting of microscopic marine plants. A similar, but smaller species is the basking shark (*Cetorhinus maximus*). While the whale shark and basking shark filter feed at, or near the ocean surface during the day, a third species, the megamouth shark (*Megachasma pelagios*), filters the water at night. It is even equipped with luminous lures around its mouth to attract larger prey, which swim towards the light. Due to their overall form, it is possible to tell that these filter feeding species have descended from predatory ancestors, but evolved to fill ecological niches that were hitherto unexploited.

▲ *Tiger sharks are good examples*
of typical sharks, which have
changed little in millions of years.

Typical sharks

Typical sharks have changed very little from ancestors that lived tens of millions of years ago. This is because their design had already been perfected by the process of natural selection, so the passage of time has seen modern species change in only minor ways, according to specific lifestyles. Typical species include the great white shark (*Carcharodon carcharias*), the tiger shark (*Galeocerdo cuvier*), the blue shark (*Prionace glauca*), the mako sharks (genus *Isurus*) and the reef sharks (genus *Carcharhinus*). All of these species are built with speed and efficiency for chasing down and dispatching prey. They have torpedo-shaped bodies with powerful tails for propulsion and blade-like fins for precise steering maneuvers.

This ability to move apace through water is known as hydrodynamics and works in a similar way to the aerodynamics of birds of prey flying through air. The idea is to create as little resistance as possible, so that energy is not wasted and momentum is maintained. Even the shark's skin is adapted to reduce water resistance or drag. It has a rough texture that traps a layer of water, so that the shark is effectively lubricated as it moves forwards.

The mouth of the typical shark is also well designed for its job. It is set beneath the nose of the fish to avoid drag and can open to the appropriate gape depending on the size of the prey. In the case of large prey, the jaws extend to ensure that a good bite is achieved. Inside the mouth there are concentric rows of razor-sharp teeth. They work in the manner of a tank-cutting saw, removing bite-sized chunks from the victim as the shark rotates its mouth by twisting from side to side. The outer teeth are allowed to dislodge as they wear out, so that newer and sharper teeth move outwards to replace them. Fossilized shark teeth are commonly found on beaches due to this conveyor belt of new teeth having been in action for millions of years.

Chasing and dealing with prey is one thing, but detecting it is another. Many sharks are endowed with large eyes for running their prey down, but vision is not effective when the water is murky or when there are low light levels due to depth or nightfall. In addition, prey may be physically hidden or camouflaged, so sharks are able to detect their food in other ways. Firstly, they have very sensitive chemical receptors (chemoreceptors) that can taste or smell the water, alerting them to the presence of blood from injured prey. Similarly, they can detect chemicals given off by other injured sharks and will quickly flee from danger if the situation arises.

Secondly, many sharks can detect the tiny electromagnetic pulses produced by the muscles in prey animals. They scan the seabed in a similar way to a metal detector and strike when they home in on the electrical signals. This makes it possible to detect animals hidden in the mud or sand. The experts at this type of hunting are the hammerhead sharks (genus *Sphyrna*). They have widened heads to increase the surface area of the skin carrying the electroreceptors or ampullae. As they cannot always see the prey they have detected, they rely instead on touch and agility to locate and eat them.

Shark relatives

The rays and skates are fundamentally similar to sharks, except that their bodies have typically become flattened to suit life spent largely on the seafloor. They are often camouflaged to match their chosen background as they are preyed upon by sharks and other marine animals. Some are armed with poisonous spines to deter would-be attackers.

Perhaps the most spectacular species is the manta or devil ray, which is a large open water species, growing to over 6.5 m (21 ft). Like the largest sharks, the manta is a filter feeder, eating plankton as well as any fish and crustaceans that happen to enter its gaping mouth.

Sawfishes (or carpenter sharks) are a peculiar group with chainsaw-like snouts used for rooting out invertebrate food species on the seafloor. They fall somewhere between the sharks and the rays and skates in terms of body form.

There are also species called ghost, or elephant sharks. The first name alludes to their iridescent and faintly luminous skin. The second alludes to their nose, which bears some resemblance to a baby elephant. They are also known variously as chimaeras, ratfish and rabbitfish. In scientific terms, they share features with sharks, rays and skates, but they also have a number of dissimilarities.

▼ *Manta rays filter feed by cruising through the oceans as if flying through the skies.*

BONY FISH

There are a great many bony fish species, as they have evolved and adapted to live in all kinds of habitats, both in salt water and freshwater. In fact, new species are still being discovered in remote and inaccessible places. Unfortunately, some are also becoming extinct because they only live in particular habitats that are now being polluted or destroyed.

Where bony fish live

Although there are different biological or taxonomic groups to which the bony fish species belong, they are also grouped according to ecological factors, such as the types of habitat they inhabit and the lifestyles they lead within those habitats.

All fish living in salt water are properly known as marine fish, while those that live in habitats such as rivers, lakes and swamps are properly described as freshwater fish. It is worth adding here, that the term 'freshwater' doesn't necessarily mean that the water is literally fresh, but rather that it isn't salty or saline. There are, of course, species that break the rules. Some species prefer brackish water, which means the water is slightly salty, where rivers pour into oceans in estuaries and deltas. Good examples are the mudskippers (Oxudercinae), which are also amphibious, meaning they are able to leave the water by using their pectoral fins as limbs.

There are also species that spend parts of their lives in either salt water or freshwater and are known as either anadromous or catadromous. Atlantic salmon (*Salmo salar*) are anadromous, as they breed in freshwater and their offspring then travel to salt water to grow and mature into adult fish. European eels (*Anguilla anguilla*) are catadromous, as they breed in salt water and their young travel to freshwater to grow and mature into adults.

As water provides a three-dimensional environment, many fish have a tendency to spend most of their time in particular regions of the water. Fish that frequent the seabed, or riverbed are described as benthic species. Some rest on the sediment, while others hide within it. Above the benthic zone there is the demersal zone and above that is pelagic zone, both of which are home to particular species of fish, too. Where the water meets the land at its edges there is a fourth region, known as the littoral zone, which also has its specific species.

In oceans, this is often described as the intertidal zone, as the water's edge moves up and down with the tide.

In order to find food, fish need to move about, or migrate. Some species move only short distances within their habitat, while others may migrate over significant distances, or even to different parts of the world. Changes in the seasons may cause these geographical migrations, across oceans or along rivers. Fish will also travel to different depths, according to day and night, because food animals do the same. This is known as circadian migration.

▶ *This adult eel is ready to leave freshwater in order to breed in the Sargasso Sea.*

eaten, although some species are more popular because they taste better and have more flesh. Most food fish are caught wild, but a few marine and freshwater species are farmed in order to provide sufficient quantities and in good condition. Fish may be eaten cooked, dried, salted, smoked, or raw in the form of sushi and sashimi. As different parts of the world have different coastlines, river systems and climates the species eaten are often different from elsewhere, too.

▶ *Yellowfin goatfish, red mullet and other species on display on a fishmonger's stall.*

DEEP SEA FISH

The deep sea, or abyss, is the last unexplored wilderness on earth. It is a vast three-dimensional environment and home to many strange fish and other organisms. As scientists explore it, they frequently discover species never seen before.

▶ *This deep sea angler fish has sharp fangs to snare prey attracted by its bioluminescent lure.*

The deep sea environment is characterized by darkness and low temperatures, because sunlight is unable to penetrate beyond the surface layers of the ocean. In addition, the weight of the water above means that very high pressures exist in the abyss.

The depth at which sunlight begins to fade is about 200 m (656 ft). This is where a zone known as the mesopelagic begins. Beneath, at a depth of 1,000 m (3,280 ft) another zone begins, called the bathypelagic. Below this, at a depth of 4,000 m (13,123 ft), the true abyss begins, otherwise known as the abyssopelagic. In places where there are additional deep sea trenches, a fourth term, hadopelagic, is used.

With no sunlight in the deep sea there is very little energy available in the form of warmth, except in places where there happens to be volcanic activity, so that water is heated by escaping lava or by hydrothermal vents. The result is that life forms tend to concentrate in places where the energy allows for a food chain to exist. In other regions, organisms are few and far between, which is one reason why deep sea fish are not well studied. In some cases, they are only known from one or two specimens encountered by chance.

Living without light and with few other fish around has its problems. Finding food is a tricky business, so deep sea fish have evolved ways to attract prey, to save them having to search in vain. They possess bioluminescence, which means they can produce light.

They use the light to attract or lure prey animals that come to investigate. When the prey gets close enough they quickly grab it. This is generally done with a large gulping mouth, so that the prey gets trapped inside, or with fearsome teeth, so that the prey is speared and cannot escape.

Of course, a similar problem arises when it comes to finding a mate. In fact, the males of some species attach themselves to females so that they are always available for fertilizing eggs because the chances of the different sexes meeting are so small. The life cycles of most deep sea fish are not known to science because no one has ever managed to make observations.

Deep sea anglerfish (order *Lophiiformes*) are well known. They use light-producing lures on the ends of fishing rod-like filaments growing from their heads – hence their common name. They have large, upward-turned mouths able to gulp prey as soon as it comes near enough. Another familiar deep sea species is the pelican gulper eel (*Eurypharynx pelecanoides*). Its scientific name alludes to its massive, pelican-like gape, which enables it to capture prey before it has a chance to swim away. Common prey fish are the lanternfish (family *Myctophidae*). They possess many small, light-producing organs called photophores, hence their common name. They use the lights to communicate with one another, which is why they investigate the lures of predators.

◀ *A barbeled dragonfish showing its greatly enlarged, fang-like teeth, seen here chasing a hatchetfish in the deep sea.*

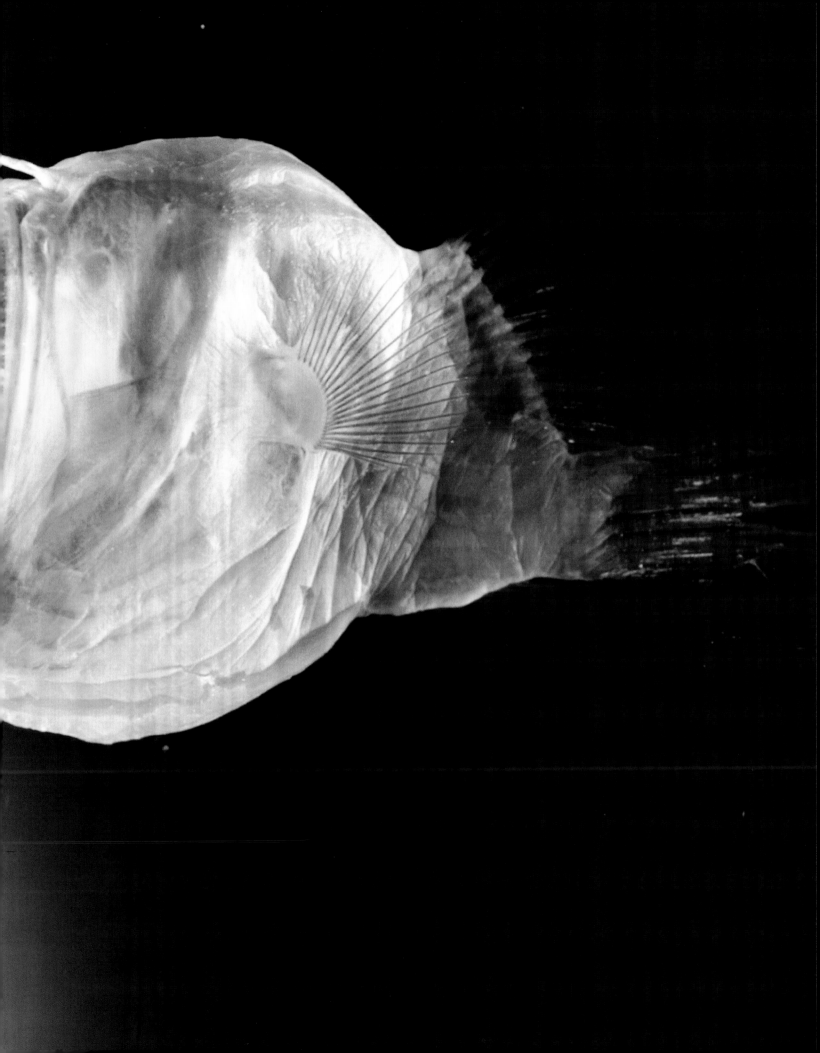

AMPHIBIANS

Amphibians consist of three orders, the newts and salamanders, frogs and toads and the caecilians. All are dependent, to some extent, on water for their development and the word amphibian comes from the Greek words *amphi* ('of both kinds') and *bios* ('life') meaning both kinds of life.

Amphibians are the descendants of the first vertebrates to move out of the water and onto the land and they still retain a strong link with water, returning to ponds, streams and rivers to breed, or depositing their eggs in saturated moss or leaf litter. The transition from small eggs to water-breathing tadpoles and eventually to miniature air-breathing adult frogs, or salamanders, is one of the most fascinating processes in nature. All adult frogs, toads, newts and salamanders are carnivores, eating mostly invertebrates, but most frog larvae (tadpoles) are herbivorous, so metamorphosis involves a switch in diet as well as in the way they breathe. Variations in reproductive mode, including parental care in a surprising number of species, provide a rich vein of study for scientists. Amphibians are equally varied in diet and in the methods they use to avoid predation. Whereas most species are camouflaged and escape notice, others are brilliantly colored to warn of dangerous toxins in their skin.

◀ *A thumbnail-sized poison dart frog, Oophaga granulifera, is a living jewel of the Costa Rican rainforest.*

Frogs

Frogs are the most familiar amphibians and are unmistakable. There are approximately 5,600 species currently recognized, making them the largest group by far. New species are being discovered all the time, but others are becoming extinct, often for reasons that are not fully understood. Frogs are found over the entire world apart from polar regions and a few remote islands that they have been unable to reach. Deserts are no barrier to frogs and there are species living in some of the driest places on Earth, but tropical rainforests are richest in species and individuals. Scientists do not distinguish between frogs and toads as they are all members of the order Anura, or tail-less amphibians.

◀ *The European common frog, Rana temporaria, a typical species found in a variety of habitats, including parks and gardens.*

Caecilians

Caecilians are an obscure and secretive group of amphibians that live hidden lives in the soil, or in the mud at the bottom of lakes and slow-moving rivers. They are elongated and have no limbs, but push themselves through the substrate using their heads as rams. They have a discontinuous distribution in South America, West and East Africa, India and parts of tropical Southeast Asia. Surprisingly, seven out of the 183 or so species live on the remote Seychelles islands in the Indian Ocean.

▶ *Caecilians are secretive burrowing amphibians that are rarely seen and which resemble earthworms.*

▶ *The male smooth newt,*
Lissotriton vulgaris, moves into
ponds and develops a wavy crest
and brighter colors during the
breeding season.

Newts and Salamanders

Newts and salamanders differ from frogs in having tails.
There are 597 species, found mostly in North America,
Europe and Southeast Asia. They are absent from much
of the Southern Hemisphere due to their evolutionary
history, most of which took place when the shape
of the continents was very different from what it is
today and the northern landmass was not connected
to the southern one. We tend to call aquatic species
newts, whereas those found on the land are called
salamanders, but many species live on the land for
part of the year and enter the water to breed and
so the distinction is not clear-cut. As with frogs and
toads, the newts and salamanders all belong to a
single order, the Caudata, or tailed amphibians.

FROGS AND TOADS

Frogs and toads are the most familiar of the amphibians. Many people first become interested in amphibians after watching the transformation from dot-like eggs suspended in a clump of frog spawn, to a wriggling mass of tadpoles and then to fully formed miniature froglets.

Frogs and toads have entered our folklore, sometimes in a positive way, as princes in disguise, waiting only for a maiden's kiss, for example, but also in a more negative way, as witches' familiars. In reality, the 5,600, or so frog species have more to fear from us than we do from them and scientists estimate that about half of all species are endangered, through habitat loss, climate change, pollution and introduced animals. In the last 30 years, a devastating fungal infection, known as chytridiomycosis, has spread around the world, decimating populations even in pristine habitats, in Central America, Australia and elsewhere. Current research is directed towards fighting this disease so that the frogs that have not already become extinct can recover.

There is a lot worth saving. Some tropical frogs are among the most colorful creatures on earth. The poison dart frogs from Central and South America come in all shades of yellow, red, orange and blue, warning predators that their skin contains potent toxins that can be lethal if swallowed. In parts of Colombia, native tribes use these toxins – called batrachotoxins – to tip their blowgun darts for hunting. Other colorful species are found among the tree frog families that occur around the world, many of which are bright green and marked with a variety of stripes, bands and spots. In contrast to the colorful poison dart frogs, these marking are intended to camouflage the frogs, many of which are defenseless and make a juicy meal for snakes, birds, small mammals and larger frogs. For the same reason, species that live on the forest floor are usually brown, often with random markings that break up their outline. Some are shaped like dead leaves, complete with stems and leaf veins and the way in which they can disappear into the background is quite amazing.

▶ *The brilliant colors of harlequin poison dart frogs warn predators that their skin contains a potent toxin.*

▲ *A small leaf-folding frog, genus Afrixalus, calls to attract a mate in the Lobeke National Park, Cameroon.*

Breeding season

Frogs are remarkable for the diversity of their reproductive methods. Although they typically breed in ponds, swamps and ditches, with aquatic eggs and tadpoles, many tree frogs, for instance, lay their eggs on leaves that overhang ponds or streams, so that the tadpoles drop into the water when they hatch. Others use their hind feet to whip up the jelly mass that accompanies the eggs into a meringue-like nest of foam that they attach to branches or float on the surface of puddles. Other egg-laying sites, used by a variety of frogs in different parts of the world, include wheel ruts, hoof prints, the empty husks of forest fruits and nuts, seedpods, snail shells and even discarded tin cans. A large number of species lay terrestrial eggs that develop directly into young frogs, skipping the free-living tadpole stage altogether, thereby breaking their link with water. Some of these lay their eggs in burrows, which can extend for up to 1 m (3.3 ft) below ground.

Parental care

A surprising number of frog species, perhaps as many as 10 per cent, show some form of parental care, in which the adults guard their eggs, or tadpoles. This can involve laying eggs on the ground and carrying the tadpoles to small bodies of water when they hatch, or carrying eggs and tadpoles on their back until they are fully formed froglets. The male Darwin's frog, from southern Chile and Argentina, picks up its eggs in its mouth and maneuvers them into its vocal pouch, where they complete their development and are spat out about 50 days later. Even more unusual are the gastric-brooding frogs from Australia, in which it is thought that the female swallows her eggs, or tadpoles, although this stage has never been observed. Her digestive juices are switched off by the substance surrounding each egg so that she does not digest them as they develop and she vomits up fully formed froglets six weeks later. Unfortunately, the only two species of gastric-brooding frogs, discovered in 1973 and 1984, are believed to have become extinct, just a few years after they were first discovered.

▼ *Poison dart frogs carry their tadpoles from the forest floor to a small pool of water to continue their development.*

▲ *Mitchell's reed frogs lay their eggs on a leaf, where the tadpoles develop until they drop into the water below.*

▲ South American horned frogs, genus Ceratophrys, have huge gapes and equally large appetites to match.

Feeding and diet

All frogs are carnivorous, eating a range of prey that depends, to a large extent, on their size. Very small species eat mites and springtails that live among the leaf litter, whereas the largest species, such as the South American horned frogs and the African bullfrog, have huge gapes that enable them to tackle other frogs, lizards and even small mammals. Most species are intermediate in size, however, and feed on insects and other invertebrates. Tadpoles, by contrast, are mostly herbivorous, scraping small fragments of algae and other plant material off rocks and leaves with several rows of rasping teeth. A few tadpoles are carnivorous and feed on small invertebrates or the eggs and tadpoles of other frogs and American spadefoot toads produce tadpoles that can switch from a herbivorous diet to a carnivorous one if the ponds they are living in begin to dry out.

Like all amphibians, frogs breathe through their skin as well as with their lungs. This can only take place if their skin is moist and they have mucous glands that secrete fluid for this purpose. If they do not replenish the water released through these glands they dehydrate, which is why frogs are most common in wet, humid places, although some species have developed behavioral and physiological mechanisms that allow them to inhabit drier habitats. Their undersurfaces are more permeable than the skin on their back so by crouching down and tucking their limbs under their bodies, for instance, they cut down on the amount of evaporation that takes place. On the other hand, if they sit on a wet surface or in a shallow puddle they can absorb water rapidly. In very dry environments, including deserts, they burrow down to a level where the sand or soil retains some moisture and they may shed several layers of their outer skin to form a waterproof cocoon around themselves. They can remain buried for many months, if necessary, in a state of suspended animation, until the next heavy rain. By contrast, species that live in very cold places hibernate for many months and some species release a form of antifreeze into their bloodstream to prevent their tissues from freezing.

Habitat and conservation

The various habitats in which frogs live often result in distinctive adaptations. Tree frogs and other climbing species, for example, have adhesive discs on the tips of their digits, which allow them to cling to smooth surfaces. Some tree frogs, from Central America and South Asia, have heavily webbed front and hind feet that allow them to glide down from tall forest trees. These two groups of so-called 'flying' frogs are not related to each other but are an example of parallel evolution, where two of more animals face similar problems and come up with the same solution. Heavily webbed feet are also characteristic of aquatic species and the members of one family, the Pipidae, have huge hind feet with extensive webbing. These species, of which there are over 30, are variously known as clawed frogs and Surinam toads depending which branch of the family they come from. They cannot feed out of the water and very rarely leave it. Burrowing frogs, by contrast, have short limbs and rotund bodies. The African rain frogs, for instance, are so chubby that the male cannot reach around the female to grasp her at breeding time and so he secretes a sticky substance from his chest that glues them together until the eggs have been laid, in this case, in burrows in the ground.

Frogs occur in most parts of the world, with two species even extending into the Arctic Circle, in Northern Europe and Canada. The tropics, especially rainforests, however, are where the greatest numbers of species live and in these places frogs fill every ecological niche, from the canopy to the ground and even below the ground. A few hectares of rainforest in South America, for example, may have over 50 species of frogs and tens of thousands of individuals. Madagascar has 235 species listed and another 150 waiting to be described and named: the actual number of species found there will probably be well over 400. These have evolved in isolation and none of them is found anywhere else. By contrast, Britain has three native species and the whole of the United States, infinitely bigger and better explored than Madagascar, has approximately 100 species. All are vulnerable to the problems that are affecting frog populations around the world and urgent measures are needed if they are not to be lost.

▶ *Several 'flying' frogs, including Rhacophorus pardalis from Borneo, use their heavily webbed feet to glide down from the forest canopy.*

NEWTS AND SALAMANDERS

◄ *The European fire salamander, Salamandra salamandra, lives in the forests of Europe and emerges to feed on rainy nights.*

Newts and salamanders are mostly small and live in leafy woodlands, emerging at night during damp weather to feed on worms and other soft-bodied invertebrates.

This description summarizes the characteristics of most species, although there are exceptions. The giant salamanders, for example, of which there is one species in China, one in Japan and another (the hellbender) in North America, are large aquatic amphibians that live in rivers and feed on anything they can capture, including fish, crayfish and large water snails. They breed in underwater burrows or caves and the male defends his 'nest' and guards the developing eggs. The Asian species are widely eaten and their numbers have fallen as a result, while the hellbenders are also suffering through the silting up of their rivers, making them unsuitable for their larvae, which live in the spaces between gravel.

The siren family, of which there are four species in the United States and northern Mexico, are elongated, eel-like amphibians with external gills, tiny front legs and no hind limbs. Like the giant salamanders, they are restricted to aquatic environments. A third family, the amphiumas, can easily be mistaken for eels, being long and cylindrical in shape, with very small, rudimentary limbs. They live in quiet, murky waters in the southeastern United States and can grow up to 1 m (3.3 ft) in length.

Most newts and salamanders, including those already mentioned, are dull brown, gray, or black in color. The red salamanders, however, are orange/red in color with random black spots and the fire salamanders are black with spots, or stripes of bright yellow. These are warning patterns and the fire salamander protects itself from predators by secreting toxins from the large glands just behind its head, which often have a particularly large yellow patch covering them. Other species, such as the sharp-ribbed newt from the central and southern Iberian Peninsula and Morocco and Anderson's crocodile newt from Japan, have poison glands along their flanks, indicated by orange spots. If the newt is roughly handled it flexes its body until its ribs, which are sharply pointed, come through the skin, piercing the glands and releasing the poison.

Reproduction

Apart from members of the most primitive families, all salamanders have internal fertilization, in which the male deposits a gelatinous package of sperm, known as a spermatophore, on the ground or on the bottom of a stream or pond and guides the female over it until she can take it up into her cloaca. She begins laying eggs some days later, often attaching them to underwater vegetation or rocks. Newt and salamander larvae are carnivorous, feeding on small aquatic invertebrates. Their development differs from that of frogs and toads because they keep their external gills until their limbs are well developed and they are more slender in shape.

Males of the species, which we call newts, are simply semi-aquatic salamanders belonging to the family Salamandridae, become more colorful during the breeding season and some species, such as the smooth newt and the crested newt, develop dorsal crests that they use to court females, performing an elaborate courtship sequence underwater in which the male uses his tail to waft waterborne scent particles towards the female before depositing his spermatophore in front of her. A few terrestrial species in this family, the fire salamander and the alpine salamander, court on land and the females retain the developing eggs in their oviducts. Some forms give birth to tadpoles whereas others wait until the young are fully formed.

▲ *Newt larvae have long, frilly, external gills and their legs develop at an early stage.*

Characteristics

Members of the Ambystomatidae are known as mole salamanders because, like many salamanders, they spend most of the year underground, in burrows, under logs, or hidden in moss and leaf litter. They all occur in North America, from Canada to Mexico and include the tiger salamander, a large and common species with a wide distribution and attractive banded coloration and the closely related spotted salamander, which has similar warning coloration to the European fire salamander.

Some salamanders never lose their external gills and retain other larval characteristics for the whole of their lives, a condition that is known as paedomorphy. Paedomorphic salamanders fail to metamorphose but live their whole lives and breed, while still in the larval state. In the case of the sirens and mud puppies, all members of the family are paedomorphic, but other families, such as the mole salamanders, include paedomorphic as well as normal species. Paedomorphic mole salamanders are known as 'axolotls, an Aztec word that applies to several species, the most common being the Mexican salamander, *Ambystoma mexicanum*. There are more paedomorphic species in other families, one of which, the olm, lives in caves in Europe. This creature has no pigment, no eyes and four spindly legs. It belongs to the family Proteidae, which also includes the mud puppies and water dogs. There are similar paedomorphic salamanders from other families living in underground streams and caverns in parts of the United States and a large species, Cope's giant salamander, from cold mountain streams in the northwest of the United States.

Salamanders can breathe in a variety of different ways. Paedomorphic species breathe through their gills and other species breathe partly through their skin and partly through lungs. Members of the largest family, the Plethodontidae, however, have completely lost their lungs and breathe through their skin and the lining of their mouth. They are commonly known as the lungless salamanders and there are nearly 400 species of them, accounting for approximately two-thirds of all salamander species. They vary in color, size and shape, although they are typically cylindrical and elongated, none more so than the worm salamander of North America. The family also includes several cave salamanders, the red salamanders mentioned above, slender salamanders, slimy salamanders and the palm salamanders from Central and South American forests.

The palm salamanders and their relatives are the only species to occur in the Southern Hemisphere. Some species carry out direct development, in which their eggs are laid on land and hatch into small salamanders, missing out the tadpole stage altogether and paralleling some of the frogs from the same region. Arboreal species have sucker-like feet and prehensile tails and all members of the family feed by shooting out projectile tongues. This family includes some of the smallest vertebrates. The minute thorius, *Thorius minydemus*, grows to only 3.3 cm (1.3 in) in total length and lives in the pine-oak cloud forest of Central Mexico. This is in stark contrast to the largest species, the Chinese giant salamander, *Andrias davidianus*, which grows to over 1 m (3.3 ft) and weighs up to 11 kg (24 lb).

▶ *Slender salamanders,*
Batrachoseps attenuatus,
from California, have
long cylindrical bodies
and tiny legs.

REPTILES

Reptiles are a diverse class of animals that are divided into four living groups, or orders. These are the turtles and tortoises, the squamates (subdivided into the lizards, snakes and a little known group called the worm lizards), the tuataras and the crocodilians.

Armored skin

All these reptiles have several characteristics that set them apart from other animals. They differ from amphibians in laying shelled eggs, or giving birth to live young. Long ago, this allowed them to break the link with water that keeps amphibians tied to moist habitats and to begin colonizing the land. The scaly covering to their skin was another important factor. Their scales can take many forms and provide reptiles with protection against water loss and an armored defense from predators. Pigment cells contained within the skin help reptiles to conceal themselves. In some species, modified scales, in the form of crests, flaps and horns are important in display and courtship and, in the turtles and tortoises, scales are fused with underlying bones to form the hard shells on their backs and undersides.

◀ *Panther chameleons, such as this male from Ambilobe, Madagascar, can be particularly colorful.*

Desert habitats

Reptiles rely on outside sources of heat to maintain their body temperature at the correct level, unlike birds and mammals, which generate their own heat through the process of metabolism. Because they do not burn up energy in order to raise their body temperature, reptiles can survive on much less food than birds or mammals – perhaps as little as one-tenth. This is an advantage for those species living in places where food is in short supply and it is for this reason that reptiles are often the dominant form of life in deserts. It also means, though, that they cannot live in cold places and so reptiles are most numerous in tropical and subtropical regions. Reptiles living in cooler regions tend to be small, spend much of their time basking and hibernate for several months in the winter. Whereas some tropical species may breed several times each year, temperate species only breed once, usually in the spring. In very cold places, such as Northern Europe, they may only breed every two, or three years.

▼ *A Bocage's wall lizard basks in the Mediterranean sunshine to raise its body temperature.*

▶ *This Nile crocodile has ambushed a herd of wildebeest as they cross the Mara River, in East Africa.*

Ferocious predators

All crocodilians are aquatic predators and none of them eat vegetation of any sort. Their prey ranges from fish and turtles to large mammals, depending on species and opportunity – although individuals may develop a preference for a particular prey, crocodilians as a whole are not choosy about their diet and eat whatever is available, including carrion. Their jaws are extraordinarily powerful, allowing them to puncture tough hide and to pull large prey beneath the surface. Because they can remain submerged for long periods of time, they kill their prey by drowning it. Small items are swallowed whole, by throwing back their head and tossing them down their throat and large items are dismembered by grasping a piece in their jaws and spinning rapidly until it breaks off. Some species cooperate to herd fish into shallows where they are more easily caught, or to induce panic into herds of mammals as they cross rivers, or drink at waterholes. One species, the West African dwarf crocodile, leaves the water at night and hunts on land.

Good parents

Despite their reputation as primeval predators, research on crocodiles in the 1970s showed that they make good parents. Females build nests out of piles of dead vegetation, or in soil and cover their eggs, numbering from 10–50, as soon as they are laid. They then stay nearby to defend the nests from other predators. When the eggs hatch, two to three months later, the young call from inside the nest and the female helps them to escape by removing some of the nest material. She carefully picks the young up in her mouth and carries them, a few at a time, to water, usually a shallow pool, or backwater. She also rolls any unhatched eggs around in her mouth until the young break free. Once all the young are out of the nest and in the water she remains with them for a period of time, ranging from a few months in the case of tropical species to two years in American alligators. Males may also stay near the young to help protect them.

Conservation

For many years, crocodiles were hunted for their skins and for sport. A number of species almost became extinct, including the Australian saltwater crocodile and the gharial. The American alligator also disappeared over much of its range and large adults became rare. Legal protection, public education, captive breeding and the establishment of crocodile farms, where a proportion could be harvested to satisfy the demand for skin and meat, helped to save them, although the Chinese alligator is still on the brink of extinction.

LIZARDS

Lizards are the most successful reptiles, showing greater diversity than other groups and a wider distribution. There are few places, except the polar regions, where lizards are not a conspicuous and important part of the fauna.

Lizards form part of the Squamata, an order that also includes snakes and worm lizards. They are the largest suborder, with 5,079 species. Not only do they occur over a greater area than any other group of reptiles, they have also moved into more niches, so there are lizards living on the ground, in trees and bushes, under the ground and in water. One species, the marine iguana, from the Galapagos Islands, even enters the sea to feed on seaweed. Because they rely on external sources of heat to maintain their body temperature, there are more lizards in the tropics, both in terms of numbers and of species, than in cooler parts of the world and some tropical regions can contain over 100 species in a relatively small area. Lizards in cooler places have evolved ways of dealing with the cold, such as small size and dark coloration, to help them warm up quickly and giving birth to live young, so that their eggs are not left to the uncertainties of the weather.

Most lizards are instantly recognizable. They are scaly, slender-bodied reptiles with a long tail and four legs. Their scales take many forms and may be small and granular or large and overlapping, smooth and shiny or rough, with a ridge running down their center. Some species, such as the chameleons, have scales of different sizes, with large, prominent ones scattered among smaller ones, while others have localized scales that are modified into spines and crests. Males of many species, including iguanas, agamas, chameleons, whiptails and wall lizards are brightly colored and they display to each other and to advertise territories. Lizards are usually active during the day and spend much of their time maintaining their body temperature by basking. In most families, the hind limbs are longer than the front ones and they are fast runners and agile climbers. These are the lizards, large and small, that are most often seen running and climbing over rocks, bushes and trees in many parts of the world, especially during sunny weather, hunting insects and other invertebrates.

◄ *A male tree agama perches on a log. During the mating season the male agama will partly turn a bright and rich blue.*

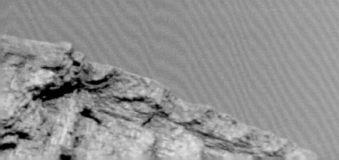

▲ *The slow-worm, Anguis fragilis, is one of a number of legless lizards that are often mistaken for snakes.*

Lizard families

Among the 27 families (20 according to some authorities and depending on the classification system used) there are plenty of exceptions to the typical lizard stereotype, however. The geckos, for example, of which there are over 1,000 members, are mostly nocturnal with just a few brightly colored diurnal species. Some are commensals of humans, emerging from their hiding places in the evening to hunt moths and other flying insects on the walls and ceilings of tropical houses and restaurants. Adhesive pads on their toes help them grip rough surfaces with ease and they can even climb over smooth surfaces, such as glass. Ground geckos lack the adhesive pads and have claws, like most other lizards, while the desert-dwelling web-footed geckos have feet that are adapted to running across the loose, wind-blown sand of the Namib Desert.

In other families, notably the skinks (Scincidae) and the anguids (Anguidae), there are species with no limbs at all. The European slow-worm, for example, lacks limbs and is sometimes mistaken for a snake. Other species have small limbs that are rarely used, but which the lizards hold against their sides when they are moving through dense vegetation or 'swimming' through loose sand. In both these families there are species with fully functional limbs, others with reduced limbs that are of limited use and some with no limbs at all, showing an evolutionary trend towards limblessness. The 36 species of flap-footed lizards, the Pygopodidae, from Australia and New Guinea, have no such variation: none of them have front limbs and their hind limbs are reduced to small scaly flaps.

Most lizards are egg layers, but there are some live-bearing species among them: whereas some families use exclusively one reproductive mode, or the other, some include examples of both types. Clutch sizes vary from one or two in the geckos, to 50 or more in monitor lizards and some agamas. Although few lizards show any kind of parental care, a few skinks and alligator lizards coil around their eggs while they are incubating and may help the young escape from the egg. Females from a number of families can lay eggs without having mated with a male, a reproductive method known as parthenogenesis. About 15 species of whiptail lizards from America, for example, are female-only species and are thought to have arisen through the hybridization of two closely related species. At least one gecko, the mourning gecko, *Lepidodactylus lugubris*, is also an all-female species and this has helped it to spread around the world because a single female, carried by drifting debris or introduced accidentally along with imported produce, is enough to begin a new colony.

Chameleons

Chameleons are familiar to most people, even if only through the medium of television. These lizards are beautifully adapted for an arboreal lifestyle, with a leaf-shaped body, grasping claws, a prehensile tail and independently rotating eyes, which they can use to look to the front and behind at the same time. Although their ability to change color is often exaggerated, they can display a variety of hues and patterns, depending on their mood and males become especially vivid when they are defending their territories, or courting a female. Chameleons feed on insects and small vertebrates, including other lizards, by shooting out their extensible tongue, which can be as long as their body and has a sticky tip. The smallest species, *Brookesia minima*, comes from Madagascar and can sit comfortably on a matchstick. Chameleons move with a slow and deliberate gait, swaying slightly to simulate a leaf moving in the breeze, but other lizards have far more energetic methods of locomotion. Some species lift up the front of their body when they run at speed, for example, so that they use only their hind feet (bipedal locomotion) and the basilisks, from Central and South America, use the same action to run across the surface of water. The flying dragons, of the genus *Draco*, have membranes of skin stretched between extra long ribs that they use to glide from one tree trunk to another in the rainforests of Southeast

Asia and a group of geckos, belonging to the genus *Ptychozoon*, from the same region, have frills of skin along their flanks, toes and tail that perform the same function.

▼ *Geckos' toes expand into flat pads, enabling them to cling to smooth, vertical surfaces.*

Tuataras

Two species of tuataras are the sole survivors of the order Rhynchocephalia (suborder Sphenodontida), relics of an ancient group that first appeared in the Mesozoic period, some 220 million years ago and spread over much of the Southern Hemisphere. Both of the surviving species belong to the genus *Sphenodon* and are restricted to small offshore islands around the coast of New Zealand, although they were widespread on the mainland until humans arrived on New Zealand, about 1,000 years ago. Although they superficially resemble lizards, they differ in their teeth, which are fused to their jaw forming a serrated, beak-like arrangement (Rhynchocephalia means 'beak head') and in addition, the upper jaw is fused to the skull and therefore not as mobile as it is in lizards.

Their natural habitat is cold, wet and windswept and they live in burrows that they sometimes share with seabirds. They lay eggs which take about one year to hatch and their growth rate is extremely slow, taking 20–35 years to reach full size, although they can breed long before this. Tuataras are thought to live for at least 100 years.

The largest lizards are the monitor lizards (Varanidae), which live in Africa, Asia and Australia. The Komodo dragon, *Varanus komodoensis*, lives on a few small Indonesian islands and is the largest known lizard. It can grow to over 3 m (10 ft) in length and although it eats mostly carrion, it is also a formidable predator and has been known to attack humans. In North America, the beaded lizards (Helodermatidae), which comprise two species, the Mexican beaded lizard and the Gila monster, are the only two venomous lizards in the world. They have grooved fangs in their lower jaws, as opposed to snakes, in which venom fangs, when present, are in the upper jaws. They are rarely seen because they are active mostly at night in the deserts of the American southwest and Mexico. Their bite, though very painful, is rarely fatal to humans.

▼ *The world's largest lizard, the Komodo dragon, is a menacing sight when stalking its prey.*

Other defensive mechanisms include camouflage, used by numerous lizards, including females of those species in which males are brightly colored. The males must make a trade-off between being seen by potential rivals and mates and being found and eaten by predators, whereas females have no such dilemma. Both sexes of the American horned lizards, genus *Phrynosoma*, however, match the gravelly substrate on which they live so well that they can be almost impossible to see unless they move. Some of them have a second line of defense in which they squirt blood from their eye sockets. Lizards from several families, including geckos and skinks, have the ability to shed their tail, a process known as caudal autotomy. This leaves a predator with a wriggling tail while the rest of the lizard makes good its escape. The tail in these species is often more brightly colored than the lizard's body, sometimes blue or pink, so that the predator's attention is directed to it. Yet other lizards try to intimidate their predators by presenting them with a cluster of spiny scales, or a crest or frill that can be erected to make them look bigger and fiercer.

▶ *Australian frilled dragons, Chlamydosaurus kingii, expand the ruff-like frill around their neck to intimidate predators.*

SNAKES

Compared with lizards, snakes have a fairly conservative 'design,' without limbs, or any of the frills, flaps, crests, or horns that decorate some of their close relatives. This has not held them back, however, and with about 3,000 species they are the second largest group of reptiles.

Worm snakes

Snakes are scaly, elongated reptiles, with a cylindrical body, a tail at one end and a head at the other. They have no limbs, external eardrums, or eyelids as a result of their evolutionary past, when their ancestors became exclusively subterranean and had no need for such luxuries. The oldest surviving families, known as worm snakes and thread snakes and numbering 545 species between them, are still burrowing snakes. These are small snakes with shiny scales and primitive eyes, that live below ground, feeding on termites, ants and their larvae and venturing onto the surface only at night or if they are washed from their burrows by flooding. Most other snakes, though, later returned to the surface and evolved new and specialized methods of locomotion and of monitoring the world around them. Some of their senses are unique while others are developed to a higher degree than they are in other animals.

Tongue-flicking

Because their eyesight and sense of hearing are poor compared with most vertebrates, smell is the most important sense for the majority of snakes. They have a specialized sense organ, Jacobson's organ, that they use, together with their tongue, to sample airborne smells. When a snake is hunting, or if it detects a change in its environment – perhaps a vibration – it flicks out its tongue and moves it up and down, picking up scent particles on the forked tip. After a few seconds, it draws its tongue back into its mouth and inserts the two tips into a pair of small openings in the roof of its mouth, which connect with Jacobson's organ. Here the scent particles are analyzed and the results passed to the olfactory part of the snake's brain.

◀ *A grass snake, Natrix natrix, pushes its head above the water and tests its surroundings by flicking out its tongue.*

▲ *The heat pit is clearly visible between the eye and nostril of this canebrake rattlesnake from east Texas.*

Heat pits

Certain species of vipers, known as pit vipers, a group that includes the rattlesnakes, use unique heat-sensing organs, known as heat pits, located between the eye and the nostril on either side of the head to detect the presence of warm-blooded prey. These organs are extremely sensitive and, by balancing the signals received on each side of their head, the snake can locate its prey and strike accurately, even in total darkness. Most pythons and boas also have heat pits, arranged along the scales bordering their mouths, lining the upper and sometimes the lower lip, but they are less sensitive than those of pit vipers.

Constriction

All snakes are carnivorous predators, eating prey that ranges in size from small invertebrates to large mammals in the case of large boas and pythons, such as the anaconda and the reticulated python, which can grow to almost 10 m (33 ft) in length. Most species are intermediate in size, however, measuring from 50 cm (20 in) to 1.5 m (5 ft) and feed on a variety of fish, amphibians, lizards, other snakes and small mammals, especially rodents. Their means of catching and subduing prey are of great interest and they have three basic strategies. Many snakes simply grasp their prey in the mouth and begin to swallow. The European grass snake, *Natrix natrix* and the North American garter snakes, genus *Thamnophis*, are in this group, feeding mostly on fish, frogs and newts. Then there are species that throw one, or more coils around their prey and constrict it until it cannot draw breath and dies of asphyxiation. These species, which include numerous medium-sized snakes, such as rat snakes and kingsnakes, as well as the large boas and pythons, do not 'crush' their prey to death, as it is popularly believed, although some small bones may get broken in the process. Finally, a relatively small proportion of snakes use venom to kill their prey. The cobras (Elapidae) and vipers (Viperidae) have the most efficient systems. Their fangs are hollow, like hypodermic syringes and the venom is actively forced through the aperture at their tips by the contraction of muscles surrounding their venom glands, which are situated towards the rear of the upper jaw. The fangs of cobras are fixed and relatively short, whereas those of vipers are long, curved and fold out of the way when not in use.

Having found and overpowered their prey, a snake's next problem is how to swallow it, bearing in mind that they have no limbs to help dismember it. They swallow it whole, a process that is facilitated by their very flexible skull and lower jaw, the bones of which can be temporarily dislocated, and by their elastic skin. These features allow them to swallow prey items that have a much larger diameter than their head and a muscular esophagus helps to pull the prey down into the stomach. Large prey is invariably swallowed head first to allow it to pass down the throat more easily. Snakes that eat exceptionally large prey may go for many weeks or even months between meals, helped by the fact that they have a very efficient digestive system that wastes almost nothing, coupled to a low metabolic rate that uses hardly any energy when they are resting. More active species, however, and those that eat smaller prey, hunt and eat most days. The African egg-eating snakes, of the genus *Dasypeltis*, feed exclusively on birds' eggs, which they swallow whole before breaking

the shell using specialized vertebrae that protrude into the top of their gullet. Because their prey is seasonal they must feed heavily for a few months so that they can store enough energy to see them through the rest of the year.

Snake bite

Venomous snakes are hazardous to humans in some parts of the world, notably in parts of Africa and Southeast Asia, where there is a large rural population that works on the land, often wearing flimsy footwear. It is estimated that 50,000–100,000 people are killed annually by snakes, but this figure would be lower with better medical facilities. The risk in westernized countries is much lower – between five and ten cases per year, on average, in each of the United States of America, Europe as a whole, and Australia (which has a larger proportion of venomous snakes than any other country).

▼ *In a battle of giant reptilian predators, this African rock python is constricting a large Nile crocodile.*

▲ *This milk snake from Mexico, seen here with its eggs, is a colorful but harmless mimic of the venomous coral snakes.*

Camouflage

As well as being highly efficient predators, snakes themselves are also preyed on, sometimes by other snakes and they have evolved a number of defensive techniques. The first line of defense is to escape notice and the great majority of snakes are well camouflaged when in their natural environment, so tree snakes are often green, for instance, whereas desert species are yellow, orange, or gray, depending on the substrate.

Warning

Other species, however, are brightly colored to warn possible predators that they are venomous and the best known of these are the American coral snakes, which belong to the cobra family. Coral snakes have rings of black, red and white (or yellow) around their bodies and, if they are attacked, they thrash around producing a show of flashing colors to startle and warn predators. Harmless species, notably the milk snakes, which live

in the same region, mimic these venomous snakes and predators are fooled into avoiding them too, hence their alternative name of 'false coral snakes.' African and Asian cobras spread a wide hood and rear up the front part of their body if they come under attack but, like most snakes, they prefer to avoid confrontation by slithering off into a place where they cannot be followed.

Shake and rattle

Rattlesnakes produce a loud rattling sound by raising and vibrating their tail, causing the segments of their rattles to click together rapidly and a group of desert vipers from North Africa, the Middle East, Pakistan, India and Sri Lanka, the saw-scaled vipers, make a rasping sound by rubbing rough scales on their flanks together as they move one section of their body against another.

Worm lizards

The so-called worm lizards are neither worms nor lizards. They comprise the third and smallest suborder of the Squamata, the Amphisbaenia, with about 160 species. They occur mainly in the tropical and subtropical parts of North and South America and the southern half of Africa, although there are five species living in the regions bordering the Mediterranean.

All worm lizards are burrowing reptiles that rarely emerge onto the surface and for this reason few people even know of their existence. Small species are easily mistaken for earthworms as their scales are arranged in rings around their bodies and many are pink in color. Three species, placed in the family Bipedidae, have a pair of stubby front limbs but no hind limbs, whereas the members of the other three families have no limbs at all. They use their heads, which have reinforced skulls, to drive a tunnel through the earth and feed on insects, worms and small vertebrates, which they drag into their tunnels. They include egg-laying and live- bearing species.

A Mexican worm lizard, or ajolote, a two-legged species that lives beneath the surface in the deserts of Baja California, Mexico.

Like lizards, snakes may lay eggs or give birth to live young and large species may produce clutches or litters of up to 100, although 5–20 is more normal. Female pythons coil around their eggs during their incubation, protecting them from predators and keeping them at a constant temperature by producing metabolic heat through shivering, but other egg-laying snakes lay them in a place where the temperature and humidity is suitable and play no further part in their incubation. Live-bearing species often bask during their pregnancy to warm their developing embryos and, therefore, to speed up their development and so this mode of reproduction tends to be more prevalent in species from cold regions. The most northerly occurring snake, for example, is the European adder, *Vipera berus*, that ranges into the Arctic Circle and is a live-bearer, as are the garter snakes that occur in North America.

▼ *A western diamondback rattlesnake forms a defensive coil with its head raised, tongue flicking and rattle vibrating.*

TURTLES AND TORTOISES

Turtles and tortoises are instantly recognizable, being the only vertebrates with a hard bony shell. The 300 or so species are divided into 13 families and they are found on the land, in the sea and in freshwater habitats.

Side-necked turtle

Strictly speaking, there is no distinction between turtles and tortoises, although in common usage tortoises are the species that live on the land and turtles are the aquatic and semi-aquatic species (except in Australia, where even the freshwater kinds are referred to as tortoises). Scientifically, they all belong to the order, Testudines. There is a major distinction between the species that retract their head straight back into their shell, the hidden-necked turtles, or Cryptodira and those that swing it to one side, the side-necked turtles, or Pleurodira.

◀ *This young Australian snake-necked turtle is protecting its head by bending its neck to the side.*

Shell as protection

The shells of turtles and tortoises are made up of 50–60 bones, some on the underside (the plastron) and some on the back (the carapace) which are connected to each other by a bony bridge at each side, between the front and back legs. The bones of the carapace are fused to each other to form a single, helmet-like covering and the ribs and vertebrae are fused to its inside surface. This gives the animal a great deal of protection against predators and most species can withdraw their heads, limbs and tails into the shelter of their shell. The North American box turtles, of the genus *Terrapene*s, which are largely terrestrial but enter the water occasionally to soak, have hinged plastrons that they can close tightly when their head and front limbs are retracted. The African pancake tortoise, *Malacochersus tornieri*, has a flat, flexible shell that allows it to wedge itself into narrow rock crevices. Some turtles have reduced shells that only partially cover the softer parts of their bodies. These include the sea turtles and some of the larger, more aggressive species such as the snapping turtles.

Sea turtles

Whereas land turtles, or tortoises, generally have high domed carapaces which are difficult for predators to grasp or smash, aquatic species have flatter shells that give them a more streamlined shape for swimming.

▲ *All sea turtles, such as this green turtle, have their limbs modified into flippers and are powerful swimmers.*

The bony shell is covered in large but thin scales, known as scutes, which give the animal its color and markings, but in the soft-shelled turtles and the pig-nosed turtle this is replaced by a covering of soft, leathery skin. Turtles are usually some shade of brown or green to match the soil, mud or vegetation among which they live, although the star tortoises from India, Sri Lanka and Myanmar (Burma) and the radiated tortoise from Madagascar have beautifully marked scutes in black and yellow and the African leopard tortoise has a speckled, horn-colored carapace. Land tortoises have thick, elephantine feet, but aquatic species have webbed feet or, in the marine species and the pig-nosed turtle, their limbs are modified into flippers. Although land tortoises are slow-moving and ponderous, aquatic turtles, including sea turtles, are speedy swimmers. Freshwater turtles can often be seen basking on rocks and logs near water, sometimes piled on top of each other to gain the best position. They are quick to tumble into the water if they are disturbed, however, and dive to the bottom.

Big and small

The smallest species is the speckled padloper, a South African tortoise that grows to almost 10 cm (4 in) in length, whereas the largest is the leatherback turtle, *Dermochelys coriacea*, a gigantic ocean-going reptile whose carapace measures up to 1.7 m (5.5 ft) in length and can weigh almost a ton (900 kg). Remarkably, the leatherback feeds almost entirely on jellyfish and sea squirts, eating up to half its body weight of these each day. The giant tortoises of the Galapagos Islands, *Geochelone nigra*, which interested Charles Darwin, can grow to 270 kg (600 lb) in weight and measure 1.2 m (4 ft) along their carapace. Their numbers declined dramatically once sailors started visiting the islands and stocking up with tortoises as a source of fresh meat, the numbers taken being in excess of 100,000. Since gaining protection the numbers have recovered somewhat and the current population probably numbers around 15,000–20,000, although some unique island races (sometimes regarded as separate species) became extinct in the meantime. Another species of giant tortoise, *Dipsochelys dussumieri*, lives on the Aldabra atoll, in the Indian Ocean (Seychelles).

Conservation

Turtles and tortoises lay eggs on land, so aquatic species have to come ashore. Turtle eggs are spherical or elongated, depending on the species and may have a brittle shell, like a bird's egg, or a flexible, leathery shell. Sea turtles often travel thousands of miles from their feeding ground to the beaches where they lay their eggs, hauling themselves up above the high tide level at night and digging a flask-shaped pit in which to lay their hundred or so eggs, before carefully covering them up and returning to the ocean by morning. Female green sea turtles lay up to ten clutches in a single breeding season, making it the most prolific reptile. Sea turtle eggs hatch after about two months and the young dig themselves out of the sand before running the gauntlet of numerous predators as they make a dash for the relative safety of the sea. Provided they survive, they take more than ten years and perhaps as long as 50 years, to reach breeding size. Much of their juvenile life is still a mystery, but they spend some of it drifting in the open ocean or floating among rafts of *Sargassum* seaweed. Hatchlings of other species remain in their nests after hatching in order to avoid cold weather and emerge the following spring. The northern Australian snake-necked turtle, *Chelodina rugosa*, is very unusual by laying its eggs in a burrow underwater. They remain dormant until the water dries up and then hatch in the mud.

Conservation is an important issue with turtles and tortoises. Despite surviving for over 200 million years, many species – perhaps as many as half of them – are in danger of extinction. The reasons for their vulnerability include their slow growth rate and late maturity, meaning that an individual has to survive a relatively long time before it can reproduce. Marine species are still hunted illegally in many parts of the world and their eggs taken, while others become entangled in fishing nets and drown. Development, agriculture and tourism have seriously reduced the habitat over which tortoises can roam and breed and because they are relatively immobile, they are unable to move to more suitable areas. Many tortoises fall victim to road traffic and bush fires. Freshwater species lose habitat as marshes and lakes are drained.

◄ *Freshwater turtles love to bask by hauling out onto a log. Painted turtles are widespread in North America.*

BIRDS

Birds, like mammals, are an evolutionary offshoot from the reptiles. They still share a number of reptilian characteristics, such as scales and a lack of true teeth, but they differ from reptiles in particular ways also. For one thing, they are endothermic (using metabolically generated heat to regulate their body temperature), which enables them to live in places that don't provide the ambient warmth that reptiles require. The most obvious detail though is feathers.

Defining birds

Feathers are known to have evolved from scales. In fact, they still are scales essentially, but rather more elaborate in their design. A number of early fossil birds, including *Archaeopteryx*, show that tree-living, or arboreal, reptiles began leaping from tree to tree, either to catch prey, or escape predators; probably both. Those with enlarged and flattened scales were able to leap that little bit farther because they were beginning to glide. Natural selection eventually caused those mutated scales to develop into feathers, as they needed to be larger, but lightweight and strong. So it was that the first birds evolved in the ancient forests. Over time they became truly aerodynamic and capable of proper flight. This ancestral species then went on to evolve into the amazing variety of species now known to science.

Birds make up an extremely successful class of animals known as Aves. Their success can be measured both in numbers of species and the wide range of habitats they have made their home. They can be found anywhere from the equator to the polar regions, from lowlands to mountain tops, on land and on water, underwater, underground, on cliff faces, in caves and in cities. Of course, most species live in woodland or grassland of some kind, but deserts, coastlines and islands are also home to birds, among other places. There are few places where birds are not found at all at some time of the year.

◀ *The hoatzin is the most primitive living bird. Its chicks have claws on their wings, demonstrating a reptilian ancestry.*

Flight and food

For many birds their ability to fly is the secret to their success. It enables them to migrate over the globe to find the best availability of food. In fact, those that can't fly often migrate to some extent, too. The importance of migration is that birds can time their reproduction to suit food abundance and give their offspring a good chance of survival into adulthood.

All birds reproduce by laying eggs, which are usually laid in a nest of some kind. Unlike mammals, female birds are not disadvantaged by pregnancy and both

▲ Redwings visit Britain in the winter from Scandinavia to feed on berries and other winter fruits.

sexes typically share the workload in terms of incubating the eggs and feeding, protecting and teaching young. Overall this allows for a high rate of reproductive success, so that bird populations can be relatively high. This means that species can afford to lose many individuals to predation, starvation, disease and weather without long-term risk to the species survival.

▶ *Bee-eaters will feed on most soft-bodied flying insects, such as this dragonfly.*

When it comes to food, different birds have adapted to eat most things. There are leaf and grass eaters, fruit eaters, seed and nut eaters, nectar eaters, insect eaters, invertebrate eaters, fish eaters, amphibian eaters, reptile eaters, bird eaters and mammal eaters. Then there are those somewhere in between, the scavengers, opportunists and omnivores, happy to consume a variety of foodstuffs, including rotting flesh and refuse discarded by people.

PASSERINES

Birds from the order Passeriformes are often collectively known as perching birds, songbirds or passerines. The term "perching birds" alludes to a mechanism found in the legs of these birds. As the weight of the body pushes down on the legs it causes a tendon to tighten, which makes the toes curl, thereby ensuring a tight grip on the birds' chosen perch. It is an important evolutionary detail as it enables these birds to roost safely while asleep, because the weight of their own slumbering bodies keeps them from falling to the ground. It is a fail-safe mechanism. Their feet have three toes facing forwards and one facing backwards, which opposes the others like the thumb on a human hand.

Outlining the passerines

The term 'songbird' alludes to a vocal organ found in the throat of these birds, called the syrinx, which enables them to produce their calls and songs. Strictly speaking, there are two suborders in this regard: oscine passerines (Old World songbirds) and suboscine passerines (New World songbirds). Birds in the first suborder have a slightly more advanced type of syrinx than the second suborder. The word oscine is derived from the Latin *oscen* for 'songbird,' and the word passerine is derived from the Latin *passerinus* which translates as 'sparrow-like.'

There are well over 5,000 species of passerines worldwide, making them the most successful order of birds. They range in size from the common raven (*Corvus corax*) at 69 cm (27 in) and the superb lyrebird (*Menura novaehollandiae*) at 100 cm (39 in), down to the short-tailed pygmy tyrant (*Myiornis ecaudatus*) at 6.5 cm (2.6 in) and the goldcrest (*Regulus regulus*) at 8.5 cm (3.3 in).

◄ *Here a blue jay is about to take a perch on the branch of a sumac tree.*

▲ *The male chaffinch is rather more colorful than the female, but otherwise very similar.*

All passerine nestlings are naked and vulnerable when they first hatch from their eggs. They are known as altricial nestlings, in contrast with precocial nestlings, such as those of chickens, which are down-covered and able to fend for themselves straight away. Due to their vulnerability, passerine birds typically build secure, cup-shaped nests in which to nurture their young in safety. In most cases the male and female birds share in the duty of tending their offspring, which is a full-time job for both as a great deal of food is required to be found. The young birds have large and brightly colored gapes and the adult birds instinctively stuff food items into the most conspicuous. That way, all of the offspring tend to get an equal share, as they don't open their mouths when they are not hungry.

Many male passerines are more colorful than their females. In these cases it tends to be the females that incubate the eggs, as they are cryptically colored so that they are camouflaged from predators while sitting. Often, though, the male's coloring is confined to the breast and the open wing, so that it is not visible when the bird is on the nest. The coloring is there to impress the female during courtship and to outdo other males competing for territory and females.

While some passerines are remarkably skilled at singing and mimicry, others are only able to produce lackluster chirps and croaks. The purpose of elaborate song in passerines has been the focus of scientific study, as it seems to go beyond simple communication. It may be that it is another way of outdoing competitors, but an ability to mimic other birds might also discourage competitors by creating the impression that a territory is already too overcrowded to bother moving in. Whatever the explanation, their songs are best heard first thing in the morning with the dawn chorus, or last thing in the day, with the dusk chorus. The songs of different species can be used for identification when the birds are not visible or when uncertain due to similarity between species. Interestingly, it has been shown that birds can have regional accents just like people.

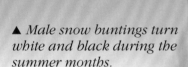

▲ *Male snow buntings turn white and black during the summer months.*

Some key groups

The warblers are a large group of passerine species, so called because they typically have a warbling song. True warblers are from the Sylviidae family and include the chiffchaff, whitethroat, blackcap and other species described as warblers, such as the willow warbler. In America, birds belonging to the Parulidae family are commonly known as warblers, too. True warblers are insectivorous and so have to migrate with the seasons to ensure a supply of insect food.

The thrush family, Turdidae, includes the blackbird, song thrush, mistle thrush, redwing and fieldfare. These are medium sized, omnivorous birds often capable of elaborate songs. Similar but smaller are the flycatcher and chat family, the Muscicapidae, which include the robin, nightingale, stonechat and spotted flycatcher. They are essentially insectivorous, although some species have adapted to a more catholic diet.

The crow family, Corvidae, includes ravens, crows, rooks, magpies and jays. These are large passerines with broad diets. They will eat any small animals they can catch and will also take carrion, nestlings and eggs. Crows have even been seen to actively hunt pigeons, by mobbing them from the air and killing them on the ground. Gamekeepers have a particular hatred of crow species as they will attack pheasant and partridge being reared for the shooting season.

▶ *Reed warblers have a song rather like two stones being repeatedly rubbed together.*

The finches are another large group of passerines. True finches belong to the family Fringillidae. They include bullfinches, chaffinches, linnets, goldfinches, greenfinches, hawfinches and crossbills. They are seedeaters, which is why they have compact bills. Upon closer inspection it is possible to see that each species has a bill designed for certain types of seeds, pips, pits and stones. This means that they can live alongside one another without competing for the same food.

Buntings and sparrows are similar to finches, but they belong to different families. Buntings belong to the Emberizidae family and tend to spend more time on the ground than finches, where they feed on fallen seed rather than collecting it from plants. Sparrows are members of the Passeridae and are related to the weaver birds, although they lack any skill at nest building, preferring instead to stuff a hole with bedding.

The true weavers belong to the Ploceidae and are famed for their ability to weave intricate nests that hang pendulously from tree branches, making it all but impossible for predators to enter. They live in Africa and Asia.

Perhaps the most intriguing passerines are the bowerbirds and birds-of-paradise. Bowerbirds, of the family Ptilonorhynchidae, are famed for the bowers that the males construct as arenas for courtship dancing. They are particularly fussy about these bowers and spend inordinate amounts of time tidying them and embellishing them with ornaments. They live in New Guinea and northern Australia. Birds-of-paradise, of the family Paradisaeidae, take a different approach. In most species, the males are adorned with extravagant plumage, while the females are quite dowdy looking birds. When females come by, the males put on outrageous and elaborate displays to show off their plumage to the best effect and hope that a female will choose to pair up.

Some of the more specialized passerines include the swallows and martins, of the family Hirundinidae, which are experts in the aerial capture of flying insects. They are so adapted to this lifestyle that their design is perfectly suited to spending a great deal

▲ *Weavers are highly skilled at weaving nests from strands of grass with their feet and bills.*

of time in flight. Swallows and martins often build nests from mud and spittle in barns or on the sides of buildings. Some nest in tunnels dug into earthy banks.

Other passerine families include wagtails and pipits (Motacillidae), wrens (Troglodytidae), dippers (Cinclidae), shrikes (Laniidae), starlings (Sturnidae), larks (Alaudidae), nuthatches (Sittidae) and tits (Paridae).

Passerines as hosts

Many passerines play host to birds from the cuckoo family (Cuculidae). Cuckoos are known as brood parasites because they lay their own eggs in the nests of other birds and remove the original eggs. The host birds are then tasked with the responsibility of rearing cuckoo chicks without knowing it. Female cuckoos match the color and pattern of the real eggs and make the switch when the host birds are not looking. The newly hatched cuckoo then ejects the other hatchling, or eggs from the nest, so that it receives all of the food and has room to grow. There are almost 60 species of parasitic cuckoo, each with its own evolved preference for using particular passerines as hosts. There are even lineages within particular cuckoo species that specialize in certain passerine species to ensure accurate egg color match. The common cuckoo (*Cuculus canorus*) may specialize in warblers, hedge sparrows or pipits for example. The unfortunate host birds are obliged by instinct to keep foraging for food as their surrogate offspring grows disproportionately large in relation to both them and the nest.

In terms of geographical distribution, the passerines are to be found in North and South America, Europe, Asia, Africa and Australasia. The only continent from which they are absent is Antarctica. In Britain, a number of passerine species are migratory. Some visit to breed in the summer months, while others come in the winter to avoid harsher weather farther north. Of course, a good number of species remain in Britain the year round too, although some travel around in winter flocks, searching for food.

◄ *This cuckoo chick requires as much food as a whole brood of reed warblers.*

FLIGHTLESS BIRDS

There are flightless bird species from a number of biological orders. They have lost their ability to fly because being able to fly is an evolutionary expense due to the high levels of energy it requires. So, in the absence of a need to fly, evolution has focused its efforts in other areas.

The prehistory of flightlessness

When birds find themselves in habitats where ground-living predators are not present, they no longer have a need to fly from danger. As a consequence, they are able to remain grounded and become larger, which has other advantages. That is the general rule with flightless birds. The classic examples were the elephant birds from Madagascar and the moas from New Zealand, both now extinct due to hunting by humans. There were also the famous dodo and its relations, the solitaires.

Typical flightless birds

Today, the largest flightless bird is the ostrich, which is large enough to see off any predator on the African plains. Similar flightless birds include the emu, the rhea and the cassowary. All share a similar design, with robust legs for running and kicking, feathers that have become fur-like and long necks for reaching the ground. They all have similar omnivorous diets, too. Kiwis are different in having long decurved bills for probing mud and sand for native worms and other invertebrates. They are also the only bird to have nostrils at the tip of the bill, so that they can smell their food, such as earthworms, insects, fruits and berries, as they forage in the leaf litter.

Other flightless birds include a cormorant, a parrot, a coot and a rail. A great many flightless bird species have become extinct over the last two centuries, partly due to persecution by man, but mainly due to the introduction of predators, such as rats, cats and dogs. That is because most lived on remote islands and went about their lives unthreatened until explorers arrived. Compounding the problem was the fact that island species had no instinctive fear because they had no experience of danger, so they were easy food for people and animals alike.

The name of the ill-fated dodo (*Raphus cucullatus*), from the island of Mauritius, has, since its demise, been used to describe people of extreme stupidity such was its own complete lack of inclination to escape when being slaughtered for food by European sailors.

▶ *King penguins are so adapted to life at sea that they are rather like upright fish when on land.*

Penguins

Perhaps the most familiar flightless birds are the penguin family (Spheniscidae), of which there are between 17 and 20 living species, depending on the classification system being used. The ancestral penguin gave up flight so that its wings could evolve into flippers, thereby enabling it to swim with supreme efficiency in the oceans to catch fish. Penguins are able to live in places where land predators are absent, so flight is not required. In addition, they can migrate via the oceans. Their main predators are seals, orcas and sharks.

A similar group of birds, the auks (Alcidae) live corresponding lives in the Northern Hemisphere. They can fly, but there used to be a flightless species, the great auk (*Pinguinus impennis*) which was hunted to extinction by man in the 19th century. Interestingly, as its Latin name shows, the name "penguin" was first used to describe this species.

▼ *The color of the scarlet ibis comes from eating red crabs found in swamps.*

◀ *Flamingos can only live on certain lakes due to their very particular diets.*

Large waders

The larger species of wading birds include herons, egrets, bitterns, storks, ibises and spoonbills. They feed on larger invertebrates, fish, amphibians, small reptiles and small mammals. The herons, egrets and bitterns (Ardeidae) have necks designed for shooting the head forwards at speed to spear prey with their sharp bills. They will stand motionless in the water waiting for unsuspecting prey to come close enough for a strike. Some species use their wings to form patches of shade over the water. This attracts prey and makes it easier for the bird to see beneath the surface. Storks (Ciconiidae) have larger bills designed for more general use in capturing slower-moving prey. Ibises (Threskiornithidae) use their long, downward curved bills in a similar way to the sandpipers, probing mud for invertebrates. Spoonbills, from the same family, have spoon-like bills for sifting food from mud.

Cranes (Gruidae) are the large equivalent of plovers. They have short generalist bills for catching a wide range of aquatic and terrestrial animals. They are also often found away from water. The most specialized waders are the flamingos (Phoenicopteridae). They have peculiar bills used for filtering waterborne food upside down. They feed on algae and small crustaceans called brine shrimps (Artemiidae). It is the shrimps that give flamingos their familiar pinkish tinge. In zoos and sanctuaries a supplement is provided in their diet to maintain the pink coloring; otherwise they turn white.

WATERBIRDS

Some aquatic birds are neither waders nor waterfowl, so they are loosely grouped together as waterbirds. They live on or around water, but comprise a range of bird types, each with their own preferences and habits.

▲ *Grebes build floating nests from vegetation to keep their eggs from predators.*

Grebes

The grebe family (Podicipedidae) comprises 20 species. They are small to medium sized birds that sit on the water like ducks and actively dive. While ducks have webbed feet, grebes have toes that have broad, leaf-like lobes. As they move their feet forward the toes fold to reduce water drag. As they move backward they open out to push the water. In this way grebes propel themselves underwater and on the surface. They have sharp bills for catching aquatic invertebrates, amphibians and fish. They nest on rafts of vegetation built well away from the waterside and safe from predators. Many species have crests on their heads and color on their necks, but otherwise they tend to be dark above and pale below.

Divers

The divers, or loons, as they are called in North America, belong to the family Gaviidae. They are similar to grebes, but their evolution has taken them to extremes in terms of their aquatic adaptation. Their legs are set so far back on their bodies that they have tremendous difficulty walking on land. As a consequence, they are always in the water, unless incubating eggs. These birds are penguin-like in their prowess at diving and hunting fish, but they use their webbed feet for propulsion rather than wings adapted into flippers. Divers are similarly rather bland in overall coloration, but they often have patches of color and pattern in the summer months. While grebes will frequent ponds, lakes and rivers, divers require fjords, lagoons and tarns. This is partly because they require a long stretch of calm water to be able to take flight.

▲ *Diver chicks use their parents' backs as places to keep safe, dry and warm.*

◀ *Water rails have long toes for walking on floating water plants without sinking.*

Rails

This family is far more cosmopolitan than grebes and divers. The Rallidae family includes coots, moorhens, gallinules, rails and crakes. They all have a similar body form, but their feet and bills are adapted to suit life in different habitats. Some are aquatic, some are semi-aquatic and others are terrestrial. Essentially they are omnivorous in diet, but their habitat determines what foods are on the menu. Many species are flattened in front profile and have head shields. This enables them to run quickly through vegetation without harm, thus avoiding predators and assisting in the pursuit of prey. Land-living species have feet similar to game birds, while water-living species have lobed feet and elongated toes. This increases their surface area and enables the birds to walk on lily pads and waterweed without sinking.

The plumage of rails varies enormously. Crakes, for example, have cryptically colored feathers to act as camouflage. Gallinules can be quite showy though, with iridescent feathers and bright red bills. Generally speaking, those safe from predation can afford to be colorful, while the others need to keep a low profile. The same goes for their voice. Water-living species can be incredibly noisy and argumentative, while those on land are more secretive and low-key.

TUBENOSES

Tubenoses are so called because they possess tubular nostrils, called naricorns, mounted above the bill. Inside the nasal cavity there is a special gland for removing salt from their blood, so they can drink seawater instead of freshwater. The salt exits the nostrils in the form of a whitish residue.

Albatrosses

Several families of seabirds make up the tubenose order, the Procellariiformes. The most impressive of the tubenoses are those from the albatross family, the Diomedeidae. They are famed for their ability to remain airborne for weeks on end by using air thermals to provide lift for their wings. In design they are similar to gliders, having very long, narrow and stiff wings with compact bodies instead of a fuselage. They are just about capable of taking off by flapping their wings but they need a good headwind to get them started.

Albatrosses need to visit land when they wish to breed. Most species nest on remote islands in the Southern Ocean, surrounding Antarctica, but some live in the Northern Hemisphere, too. The number of albatross species is a matter of some debate, with some sources recognizing 22 extant species while others retaining the traditional 14 species classification. All are large birds, ranging from the enormous wandering albatross (*Diomedea exulans*) with a wingspan of up to 3.5 m (11.5 ft), to the light-mantled albatross (*Phoebetria palpebrata*) with a wingspan of about 2 m (6.5 ft).

Albatrosses feed by skimming fish, squid, krill and jellyfish from the ocean surface. This has led to many fatalities from pollution, because the birds pick up and swallow floating pieces of plastic bags and other flotsam. Once inside their stomachs it blocks the alimentary canal and the birds die from starvation. Albatrosses have also become hooked on fishing lines when they attempt to take fish that have been line-caught from boats and ships.

◀ *Albatrosses have evolved to travel enormous distances over oceans in order to find food.*

Fulmars, petrels, prions and shearwaters

This family of birds, the Procellariidae, comprises species similar to skuas, gulls and terns, but they have more compact bodies, narrower wings and those tubes on the upper bill. Like albatrosses, they are built for long periods out to sea, where they feed on similar but smaller prey. The largest species are the two giant petrels, of the *Macronectes* genus, which have a wingspan of up to 2 m (6.5 ft). The smallest are the two prions, of the genus *Pachyptila*, with wingspans of up to 60 cm (24 in).

Fulmars are famed for their ability to spit out vomit. As a defense mechanism, the young eject a foul-smelling oil when they feel threatened in their nests, which are positioned on cliff ledges. Potential predators leave them well alone as a result.

◀ *Fulmars are similar to gulls but they don't have any black on their wing tips.*

Storm-petrels and diving-petrels

Storm-petrels (Hydrobatidae) are unlikely-looking seabirds, as they are rather delicate and they hover above the surface while treading the water with their feet. They are butterfly-like, or bat-like in their movements. They feed on zooplankton. Diving-petrels (Pelecanoididae) are more compact, rather like little auks. This is because they actively dive below the surface, using their stubby wings as paddles in the same way as auks. This is an example of convergent evolution, where unrelated species have become similar in form and function because they have adopted similar lifestyles. Diving-petrels live in the Southern Hemisphere, auks in the Northern Hemisphere.

▶ *Storm-petrels specialize in picking small planktonic animals from near the water's surface.*

PELICAN CLAN

The pelicans and their relatives (Pelecaniformes) are fish-eating birds that typically dive for their prey. Diving may take place from the air, from the water's surface, or occasionally from a perch. They have 'S' shaped necks for thrusting their heads forwards to grab fish. They often have a slight hook at the end of their bill.

Pelicans

The pelicans themselves (Pelecanidae) are famous for having very long bills with stretchable throat pouches to enable them to swallow surprisingly large fish. They will also eat amphibians and other animals. To keep their plumage water resistant, pelicans use their bills to rub preen oil on their feathers. However, they need to remove themselves from the water frequently to avoid becoming waterlogged. They often fish in gangs by encircling shoals of fish and splashing the water to scare the fish towards a central point, where there is a free-for-all to catch as many fish as possible.

There are eight species of pelican. There is some variation in size and coloration, but otherwise they are very similar in form. Some are ground-nesting, while others nest in trees. There are usually two chicks. Unusually, for waterbirds, the hatchling young are naked, or altricial, so they need to be protected by the parents until they are ready to fledge the nest.

Cormorants and shags

There is no biological distinction between the terms 'cormorant' and 'shag.' They are synonymous like 'pigeon' and 'dove.' These birds typically have glossy, dark plumage and a crest on the head. They sit low in the water, because their feathers are not very good at repelling water. This helps with diving for prey, as it means less effort fighting against buoyancy. However, it also means waterlogged plumage, which is why

◀ *Pelicans have large bills, so they can carry food back to their hungry chicks in one go.*

these birds are often seen drying themselves in a cruciform posture, while sitting on a perch.

Colonies of cormorants and shags (Phalacrocoracidae) tend to have traditional breeding grounds. This means that thick layers of guano (bird droppings) build up. At one time, ships were sent to collect this guano, which was valued as a fertilizer for crops.

The darters (Anhingidae) are cormorant-like birds that specialize in fishing freshwater rivers, as opposed to marine habitats. There are four species, from the Amazon basin, Africa, Asia and Australasia.

Gannets and boobies

These birds belong to the family Sulidae and are very similar in form. It has been suggested that the term 'booby trap' alludes to the stupidity of boobies as they will readily alight on ships, where sailors used to ensnare them for food with a rope noose (the booby trap) around the leg.

Gannets and boobies are experts at plunge diving for fish. Having spotted fish while in flight, they form a dart shape, with bill held forward and wings held back. Their heads have evolved shock absorbers, so that they are not stunned by the impact as they enter the water at high speed. Once in the water they will pursue fish and then heave themselves back to the surface before taking to the wing again.

▼ *Blue-footed boobies are not noted for their intelligence, they can be very tame and therefore easily captured and killed.*

BIRDS OF PREY

The term 'birds of prey' is an umbrella name applied to birds that hunt, kill and eat other animals: the raptors. Most prey on mammals, birds and reptiles but a few prey on fish, amphibians, insects and even worms and snails. Some specialize in eating carrion.

The taxonomy of birds of prey is the cause of considerable argument among zoologists. This is because convergent evolution seems to have arrived at similar designs for birds descended from different origins. Genetic evidence has shown that falcons may be more closely related to parrots than eagles and hawks, for example and that American black vultures may be more closely related to storks than other raptors. When animals adopt similar ways of life they can often appear so similar due to the process of evolution by natural selection that only genetics can reveal the truth. Arguments are set to continue.

◄ *In terms of worldwide distribution, the osprey is one of the most widespread birds.*

Accipitridae

This is the most diverse of the birds of prey families. Scientists currently include eagles, buzzards, hawks, kites, harriers and Old World vultures in this family. They range in size considerably and generally feed on other animals appropriate to their size. They all have wings that end in splayed feathers when in flight, as opposed to falcons which have pointed wing tips.

Hawks and harriers are small to medium sized. They are more specialized hunters than eagles, for example. Hawks tend to hunt tree-living mammals and birds in forested places, where they are experts at flying between branches. Harriers tend to hunt animals in savanna and grassland, where they are able to hover and search for movements.

Kites and vultures are primarily scavengers. They patrol the terrain in search of dead and dying animals and congregate to feed. Kites feed on small to medium sized carcasses while vultures feed on large ones. That is why they have naked heads and necks, to prevent their plumage from becoming clogged with blood and other fluids as they plunge their bills inside the dead animal to feed on organs and entrails.

Falconidae

This family of birds is home to falcons, kestrels and hobbies. These names are synonymous really, as the species are all very similar in form, varying mainly in color and size. These birds have a distinctive silhouette in flight, with scimitar-shaped wings, designed for fast flying. They also have short necks and neat tails. They have characteristically large eyes, which give them extremely acute vision for spotting and tracking prey. This might be a mammal, a bird, a reptile, or an insect, depending on the species. The hunting technique is to strike with surprise and force, by swooping out of nowhere very fast.

Eagles and buzzards are the heavyweight hunters. They tend to hunt down medium to large-sized mammals, depending on their own size. Their vision is several times better than humans in terms of magnification and they share our binocular vision, which means that they can accurately judge distances. They strike with their feet, using their momentum to stun and kill prey before it has a chance to escape. They also have talons for securing prey should it fail to die immediately and a hooked bill for ripping at the flesh.

▲ *Red kites used to be very common birds as they fed from kitchen middens or refuse heaps.*

The peregrine falcon (*Falco peregrinus*) is famed for being the fastest animal on the planet. It achieves its record-breaking velocity by falling from the sky like a stone by closing its wings. It then strikes another bird from above with its clawed feet and the prey is killed instantly. Kestrels, also from the *Falco* genus, are noted for their ability to hover, even in the absence of a headwind. They do so instead of perching in order to spot small mammals on the ground. Smaller species, such as hobbies and merlins, will hunt flying insects such as beetles and dragonflies.

Cathartidae

This is the family of New World vultures, as distinct from Old World vultures. Some confusion can arise because North Americans sometimes use the term 'buzzard' or even 'crow,' as a throwback to the arrival of European settlers who were reminded of birds from their homelands. They are similar in appearance to other vultures but not closely related, demonstrating convergent evolution due to chosen lifestyles.

There are seven species in this family. The most widespread is the turkey vulture (*Cathartes aura*) with a range stretching from Canada to the southernmost tip of South America. The most impressive are the condors, of which there are two species: the Californian (*Gymnogyps californianus*) and the Andean (*Vultur gryphus*). The latter is reckoned to have the largest wing surface area of any living bird. It uses its enormous wings to ride the thermal air currents rising from the mountains. By flying at high altitude it is able to reconnoiter large areas of t errain and locate carcasses 16 km (10 mi) distant by observing the behavior of other scavenging birds.

The most striking species is the king vulture (*Sarcoramphus papa*), which lives in and around the Amazon basin. It has a three-tone body and wings in gray, black and white. Its head appears to have been painted with a palette of reds and yellows and it has straw-colored eyes.

Strigidae and Tytonidae

These are the nocturnal birds of prey: the owls. There are essentially two types of owl – true, or typical owls (Strigidae) and barn owls (Tytonidae). Typical owls, like the tawny owl (*Strix aluco*), have cryptically colored plumage to help them blend into their habitat as camouflage during the day when they are asleep. There are species that live in woodland, desert, grassland, marshland and even tundra. Barn owls,

typified by the distinctive and much loved barn owl (*Tyto alba*) have heart-shaped faces and their plumage is more uniform in color as they rest in tree holes.

Most owls prey on small rodents, reptiles and invertebrates. They have extremely effective eyesight because their large eyes make the most of any available light. They also have offset ears, enabling them to locate sounds up and down as well as left and right, so that they can pinpoint an attack accurately. They have feathers with special serrated edges that reduce any noise created by their wings, enabling them to hunt by stealth. Prey animals, once killed, are eaten whole.

▶ *The head tufts of the long-eared owl actually have nothing whatever to do with hearing.*

GAME BIRDS

These birds have their common name because the term 'game' applies to animals shot for sport or food. In biological terms, they belong to the order Galliformes. This order contains a wide variety of bird groups including pheasants, partridges, quails, megapodes, turkeys, grouse, guinea fowl, chickens, jungle fowl, peafowl, francolins and guans.

Typical game birds

The reason why these birds are popular for sport and food is that they are ground living. They are able to fly, but they are reluctant to do so because they tend to be heavy in the body so that flying takes a good deal of effort. As a consequence, they have plenty of flesh to eat and they usually only take to the wing when flushed from a hiding place. These attributes mean that the hunter has to be quick with the gun, but is rewarded with a bird for the table.

Game birds are primarily seedeaters and herbivores, but they also eat many insects and other invertebrates. They forage for food in thickets, undergrowth and grassland, eating anything suitable. Their legs are robust and built for scraping the ground as well as running. By disturbing the soil and humus they uncover items of food that other birds would miss.

Most species are ground nesting and typically it is the female that does the incubating. This is self-evident by their cryptic plumage, which makes them blend into the ground litter when they lie on their eggs. By contrast, the males are often quite colorful and showy birds. They use their plumage to "impress" the females. The theory is that the males risk predation by being easy to locate, so the birds with the most outstanding plumage (literally) are perceived by the females to be the more virile and therefore better choices as mates.

Males seldom have anything to do with protecting or raising young though. The chicks hatch ready to leave the nest and follow the mother bird, on whom they rely for protection and to teach them where and how to find food. Broods are typically high in number because so many are preyed upon before they have a chance to reach adulthood. If one considers that only two are required to replace the adults, over their entire breeding life, for a stable population to remain, then it is easy to see that survival rates are very low.

▼ *The red jungle fowl is clearly the ancestor of domestic chickens and bantams.*

Pheasants

The most striking of the game birds are the pheasants. Some are so beautiful to the human eye that they are kept as living ornaments for the garden. Such species include the golden pheasant (*Chrysolophus pictus*) and Lady Amherst's pheasant (*Chrysolophus amherstiae*). The most prized of all though, are the peafowl, of which there are two species: the green peafowl (*Pavo muticus*) and the Indian peafowl (*Pavo cristatus*). In both species the male, known as the peacock, has a spectacular train of iridescent, eyed feathers, in green and blue, which can be erected and fanned out as part of a courtship display for the females.

▶ *Of all the pheasants, the peacock is surely the most beautiful.*

SEABIRDS

These are the birds that inhabit coastlines. The term 'seabird' can apply to any marine bird, but here we discuss the gulls, terns, skuas and auks. Most species live and breed in coastal areas. These may be cliffs, sand dunes or the beaches of offshore islands. Many species feed on fish, but some are predators, pirates, thieves and scavengers.

Gulls

Gulls, or seagulls, as they are often called, come in a variety of sizes, but for the most part species are essentially similar to one another. Most species have gray backs and white bodies, but a few have blackish heads and some are sooty all over. Gulls are opportunists, feeding on a variety of foodstuffs.

▲ *An Arctic tern has just managed to catch a sand eel for its waiting offspring.*

This has made them very successful in some places, because they will readily eat human food waste. Larger species will also rob eggs and chicks from the nest of other birds, as well as food that they attempt to bring to their nests.

Gull chicks typically peck at their parents' bills when hungry. This causes the parent birds to instinctively regurgitate the contents of their stomachs, so that the chicks get to eat food that has already been partially digested. They hatch ready to walk and they use their camouflaged feathery down to hide themselves from danger when the parents are away looking for food. Gulls belong to the family Laridae.

Terns

Terns are similar to gulls, except that they are generally daintier. They usually nest in colonies, so that predators can be fended off by parent birds that happen to be present at the time of an attack. Terns feed on small fish in the main, such as sand eels, which they dive for in shallow water. Like gulls, there are many species of terns (Sternidae) and they also live in many parts of the world. The Arctic tern *(Sterna paradisaea)* is famed for its long migration between the Arctic and Antarctic regions. There is also an Antarctic tern but it doesn't migrate the same distance in reverse.

Skuas

These birds are similar to gulls in build and size, but they tend to be brownish in color. These birds specialize in the opportunistic harrying of other seabirds to steal food, eggs and chicks. They will also eat carrion, such as dead seals, whales, sea turtles and birds. They are the cleanup crew. In America, the smaller species are often known as jaegers. There are seven species of skua in the family Stercorariidae.

Auks

These birds are essentially the equivalent of penguins in the Northern Hemisphere. With the exception of the only flightless species, the recently extinct great auk, all auks are able to fly, but they are otherwise very penguin-like. They dive and swim underwater to catch fish, and they have the same countershaded bodies; dark above and pale below. Puffins (genus *Fratercula*) are noted for their decoratively colored bills during the breeding season. Auks belong to the Alcidae family. Due to their small wings, all auks fly with very fast wing beats in order to create the lift they need to remain airborne.

▶ *Puffins only sport brightly colored bills during the breeding season over the summer.*

FRUIT-EATING BIRDS

As their collective name suggests, these birds like berries and other fruit. In fact, they also eat buds, shoots, grasses and seeds. In addition, they supplement their diet with insects and other invertebrates to be certain of getting enough protein and fat.

Pigeons

There are over 300 species of pigeon and dove. The terms are interchangeable as demonstrated by the town pigeon, whose wild counterpart is the rock dove. Pigeons and doves are the only birds capable of sucking up water, as opposed to filling their bills and tipping their head back, as other birds do. This gives them the ability to take water quickly and thus reduce the risk of predation.

▶ *Pigeons and doves vary to some extent in size and color, but they are easy to recognize.*

A species known as the passenger pigeon (*Ectopistes migratorius*) was probably the most numerous bird on the planet in the early 19th century, yet it became extinct in the first decade of the 20th century. Its success was its downfall, because it decimated crops and became public enemy number one in North America. Wholesale slaughter was sanctioned by the US government, but no one ever thought to tell people to stop shooting.

Another pigeon that became extinct was the famous dodo (*Raphus cucullatus*). It became oversized and flightless on the island of Mauritius and was hunted as food by early sailors. Neighboring islands had similar species, such as the Rodrigues solitaire (*Pezophaps solitaria*), that also vanished.

Pigeons have a unique way of feeding their young. They produce a pulp from the lining of their throats, called 'pigeon milk.' It means that the adult birds can convert foodstuffs that would otherwise be indigestible to their offspring. The adults open their bills and the young birds feed by inserting their own bills to the back of the throat. Pigeons, doves, dodos and solitaires belong to the Columbiformes order.

The woodpecker family, the Picidae, includes woodpeckers, flickers, sapsuckers, piculets and wrynecks. Species vary considerably in size from that of a sparrow to that of a crow. They typically have black, white, or green coloring and patterning on their plumage. Many species have a patch of red or yellow on the head and this is usually more extensive in the male.

Toucans

These birds have characteristically enormous bills in relation to their body size. The reason is that they need long bills to reach fruit hanging from the branches of tropical trees. If their bills were long and narrow they would lack the strength to pluck the fruit, so they have evolved for strength but are also very lightweight. The bills also come in handy for picking insects and reptiles from the canopy. While pigeons build their nests in the foliage of trees, toucans choose to build their nests in tree holes. As their bills are not designed for chiseling wood, they either use natural hollows, or they commandeer old nest holes of woodpeckers.

Toucans belong to the family Ramphastidae and are popular birds with zoological parks because they are very colorful and pleasant natured. The toco toucan (*Ramphastos toco*) is a familiar species and there are seven similar species in the same genus. There are also mountain-toucans (genus *Andigena*) and green toucanets (genus *Aulacorhynchus*), which are smaller than typical toucans. Toucans have feet with two toes pointing backwards and two forwards. This provides a secure grip when the birds are performing acrobatics to reach food.

▶ *The toco toucan is a familiar bird from zoo aviaries and children's natural history books.*

PARROTS

Birds belonging to the Psittaciformes order all have robust bills designed for dealing with hard seeds and nuts. This gives them a feeding ecological niche that most other birds cannot fill. Many species have brightly colored plumage and are intelligent enough to mimic the human voice, making them very popular pets. They also form close bonds with people because most species are social birds.

Included in the Psittaciformes order are macaws, parrots, parakeets, cockatoos, budgerigars, lorikeets, lories and lovebirds. As they come in a range of sizes and live in different forests around the world, they have specialized in eating the seeds and nuts of different plants. They will also eat fruit, buds, shoots and insects.

Feral parrots

There have been many escapes of captive parrot species in places where they are not indigenous. In some places they have consequently become introduced and established populations. The classic example is the rose-ringed or ring-necked parakeet (*Psittacula krameri*). This species, which originates from central Africa and India, has managed to survive in several European cities, including Barcelona and London. The reason for its success is its ability to feed on human handouts of bread, cake and fruit. Also, city parks tend to have large trees with suitable hollows for nesting and few predators. In addition, people favor them over pigeons and sparrows because they are pretty, even if they are rather raucous and noisy.

Beautiful parrots

The macaws are the most striking parrots, as they are large and very brightly colored, with blues, reds, yellows and greens. Species from the *Ara* genus are those most often seen in zoos and private collections. They include the blue-and-yellow (*Ara ararauna*), the scarlet (*Ara macao*) and the military (*Ara militaris*). They are so closely related that it is possible to crossbreed hybrid specimens with a spectrum of color variations.

▶ *The rose-ringed parakeet is one of the few parrot species that has successfully adapted to living in urban areas.*

Unusual parrots

Although most parrots live in forests, there are a few exceptions to the rule. In Australia, a number of species have adapted to life in the outback, which is a mixture of scrub, eucalyptus forest and desert. They include the sulphur-crested cockatoo (*Cacatua galerita*) and the wild budgerigar (*Melopsittacus undulatus*). In New Zealand, there are species adapted to mountainous terrain. One species is the kea (*Nestor notabilis*). Another is the very unlikely owl parrot or kakapo (*Strigops habroptila*), which is flightless, nocturnal and lives in a burrow.

Many parrot species have become extinct from islands in the South Pacific Ocean. This is because they had evolved to live in relatively small pockets of habitat.

▲ *This kaka from Stewart Island is very similar to the extinct Norfolk Island species.*

The arrival of Europeans resulted in habitat destruction and the introduction of predators and disease. An example is the Norfolk Island kaka (*Nestor productus*). Its habitat was destroyed by British convicts forced to settle and make new lives for themselves. They needed to clear the forest to find timber for houses and to create fields for planting crops, so the kaka found itself with nowhere to nest or feed and extinction was inevitable.

WOODPECKER CLAN

As their name implies, these birds are known for their ability to chisel wood with their bills. They do so for two reasons: to extract wood-boring insect larvae as food and to excavate nest holes in the trunks of trees.

Woodpeckers

Woodpeckers have specially designed skulls to cope with the shock of repeatedly hammering their beaks against the surface of trees. The brain and eyes are protected from damage as a woodpecker may peck as rapidly as 20 times a second. In addition, the wood is not always rotten, so the impact would shatter the head of another type of bird.

To enable them to extract insect grubs, woodpeckers also possess stiff, pointed tongues with serrations on each side, which they use to spear their prey. As this type of tongue is not fleshy, it cannot be extended like the tongue of a human, so the solution is to have a cavity that allows the tongue to curl up behind the brain when it is not in use.

The feet of woodpeckers are arranged with two toes pointing forwards and two pointing backwards. This means that the birds always have a good grip in the tree bark, whichever way round they are orientated. In addition, they have stiff tails to act as props, so that the birds can form stable tripods when they are climbing, chiseling or feeding their young.

◀ *This green woodpecker has the typical pose of a woodpecker looking for its next tree.*

The woodpecker family, Picidae, includes woodpeckers, flickers, sapsuckers, piculets and wrynecks. Species vary considerably in size from that of a sparrow to that of a crow. They typically have black, white, or green coloring and patterning on their plumage. Many species have a patch of red, or yellow on the head and this is usually more extensive in the male.

Alternative diets

Not all woodpeckers feed on insect grubs. Sapsuckers (genus *Sphyrapicus*) drill series of holes in trees so that sap oozes out as their main food source. The acorn woodpecker (*Melanerpes formicivorus*) drills holes for storing acorns. Many species forage for food on the ground, too, where they will eat all manner of insects and other invertebrates. A particular favorite is ants. The green woodpecker (*Picus viridis*) has a fondness for wood ants (genus *Formica*) which build nest mounds in forests. The woodpecker feeds on the adult ants as well as the larvae and pupae. It even utilizes the formic acid sprayed by the ants as a defense. By folding its wings over the ants, its feathers get sprayed and this helps to rid the plumage of bird lice.

Wrynecks

Wrynecks are somewhat different from true woodpeckers. They have cryptic plumage and they cannot chisel wood, except for very soft rotten wood. Interestingly, as a defense mechanism, they have evolved to mimic snakes when disturbed in their nest holes. They twist and turn their heads and make a hissing noise, which, along with their head markings is enough to deter most predators. Their genus name, *Jinx,* has become a term used for placing bad luck spells on people and stems back to medieval times when people believed wrynecks to have baleful powers due to this unusual behavior.

▶ *An acorn woodpecker at its nest hole, chiseled into the trunk of a dead tree.*

◀ *Wrynecks have cryptic or camouflaged plumage to hide them from predators.*

KINGFISHER CLAN

The birds in this group are typically hole- or burrow-nesting birds, renowned for their lack of cleanliness and stench. Their nests become soiled with excreta and detritus from the food they feed their young, which may be fish, amphibians, reptiles, other birds, insects and other invertebrates. All in all, the nursery is a stinking mess by the time the young fledge. The Coraciiformes order includes kingfishers, rollers, bee-eaters, hoopoes and hornbills.

Kingfishers

These birds are stocky with disproportionately large heads and bills. As their name suggests, they typically specialize in catching fish. They do this by plunge diving from a perch, or by hovering above the water. The prey is then killed with a strike to the head and swallowed head first. Not all kingfishers actually fish though.

The kookaburras (genus *Dacelo*) are more versatile and will eat a variety of land animals. Many kingfishers have patches of iridescent blue and orange on their plumage. The Eurasian kingfisher (*Alcedo atthis*) is a popular bird due to the flash of color seen when it darts along the riverside.

Rollers and bee-eaters

These birds are similar to kingfishers, but are less robust in physique, more like jays. They also have iridescent blues and greens in their plumage. The name 'roller' alludes to their courtship behavior, as they roll in the air. The birds have a preference for flying insects, such a dragonflies, beetles and flies.

Bee-eaters are so called because they do indeed eat bees. They catch the bees in their bills while in flight and then wipe them on a perch. This causes the bees to lose their stings, thus rendering them perfectly harmless and ready to be eaten. Bee-eaters are even more magnificently colored than kingfishers and rollers. Some species display a

◀ *The common kingfisher is a small but very striking bird with its complementary colors.*

▲ *Front and back views of European bee-eaters, showing the spectrum of colors in the plumage.*

spectrum of colors. The European bee-eater (*Merops apiaster*) has blue, green, yellow, red, white and black in its plumage.

Hoopoes

The hoopoe (*Upupa epops*), the only extant species in the family Upupidae, is a curious and unmistakable bird. It has heavy barred wings, in black and white and a large crest of feathers that can be raised to resemble a Mohawk hairstyle. As one might guess, it has a distinctive 'hoopoe' call. As the birds are conspicuous and eat animals that might be considered agricultural pests, they have long been held in high regard by farmers.

Hornbills

Hornbills are large birds compared with their cousins. They have the curious behavior of lining the entrances of their nest holes with mud, so that the females are trapped inside and fed by the male through a small aperture. This is to prevent predators getting at the eggs and young while vulnerable. Eventually the females are released, when the young take up too much room inside. Some scientists are of the opinion that this behavior also helps to fend off other hornbills, as competition for suitably large nest holes is very intense. There are over 50 species of hornbill and all live in the Old World.

▶ *Hornbills have very large, but lightweight bills, much like those of toucans.*

HUMMINGBIRDS AND SWIFTS

Despite their apparent dissimilarity, hummingbirds and swifts are descended from a common ancestral bird. The thing that gives it away particularly is their shared prowess at flying. Both types of bird are capable of aerobatics in flight because they have universal shoulder joints that enable them to twist and turn their wings in ways that other birds cannot manage.

The wings themselves are quite stiff in hummingbirds and swifts, because it is the shoulders that give them their maneuverability. Both types of bird also typically have very small legs and feet and short tails. They also both have inset eyes to provide stereoscopic vision for accurate feeding. In the case of hummingbirds, this is the precise and rapid positioning of the bill to sip nectar from flowers and with swifts it is the pinpoint capture of flying insects at high speed. Both types of bird also build cup-shaped nests and lay small eggs.

The evolutionary driver that separated the two branches was evidently food preference. It seems that the ancestral species was more of a generalist that caught insects in and around plants. Then one race specialized in catching insects from flowers and inadvertently supplemented its diet with nectar. The other moved away from the plants in pursuit of the insects as they traveled through the air. In time, the two races became subspecies and then separate species. Those two new species then diversified into the families of hummingbirds and swifts we have today.

▲ *This mountain-gem hummingbird hangs motionless on its rapidly flapping wings.*

Hummingbirds

Hovering takes up a great deal of energy, so hummingbirds (family Trochilidae) need to be small and lightweight to make it worthwhile eating nectar. That is why they include some of the smallest bird species known to science. Some hummingbirds specialize in feeding from particular types of flower, while others are more adaptable. This explains why they display a wide variety of bill lengths. There are an amazing 339 recognized species of hummingbird and all come from the New World. Many have plumage embellished with beautiful iridescent colors, including reds, greens, blues, yellows, oranges and purples. Their skill in flight is such that they are the only birds capable of flying backwards, which is essential for visiting numerous flowers with efficiency. They hover by moving their wings in a paddling motion as if the air were water, being pushed downwards.

Swifts

Swifts, unlike swallows and martins, with which they share a passing resemblance, flap their wings in a way that makes them appear out of time. This is because they use their wings to steer as well as propel themselves, having relatively small tails. They have a wide gape to catch airborne insects and bristles above the bill to protect the eyes. Swifts are so at home in the air that some species are known to sleep in flight. If they have the misfortune to crash-land, they find it very difficult to take to the wing because their legs are too short to give their wings enough clearance from the ground.

▶ *Swifts are extremely adept fliers, chasing insects with amazing agility and speed.*

MAMMALS

Mammals are vertebrates that feed their young on milk produced by mammary glands on the female's body. Mammals are also unique because they can maintain a constant body temperature even when the surrounding temperature changes.

Scientists have identified about 5,000 different species of mammals that range in size from the tiny Kitti's hog-nosed bat, which measures about 4 cm (1.6 in) across, to the truly enormous blue whale, which can be more than 30 m (98 ft) long.

Mammal groups

Different mammals are divided into groups of related animals. These include bats (mammals with wings that can fly), carnivores (mammals with sharp canine teeth that feed almost exclusively on meat), cetaceans (mammals that live in the oceans but breathe air using lungs), insectivores (mammals that feed mainly on insects and worms), rodents (small mammals with gnawing incisor teeth) and ungulates (hoofed mammals that use their grinding teeth to break down tough plant food).

◄ *A female mountain gorilla holds onto her three-month old newborn. The young gorilla remains with its mother for four years.*

Mammal evolution

Experts think that mammals developed from a group of ancient reptiles called therapsids. The evolutionary change that set mammals apart from these early reptiles took place during the Triassic period (between 250 and 200 million years ago). This included a hinged jawbone, which allowed mammals to chew their food and the ability to regulate their own body temperature, which allowed mammals to keep warm when the Earth's climate cooled during the Jurassic and Cretaceous periods.

▼ *Leopards are adept climbers and will drag their prey up trees to avoid scavengers, such as hyenas.*

Keeping warm

The ability to keep a constant body temperature is one of the keys to the success of the mammals. It has allowed them to exploit many different parts of the world, from the depths of the ocean to the tallest treetops. A mammal can maintain its body temperature in many ways. Physical changes include raising, or lowering the metabolic rate, opening, or narrowing blood vessels near the skin, shivering, sweating and panting. Sociable mammals huddle together when it is very cold, while others avoid the heat by resting in the shade or hiding in burrows. Some mammals have specific adaptations to exploit very hot, or very cold places. Desert mammals usually have light brown fur to reflect the sunlight, or large body parts, such as ears, to radiate heat away from the body. Mammals that live in the polar regions often have thick fur, or layers of blubber under the skin to insulate them from the cold.

Oryx at risk

One of the most endangered grazing antelopes is the Arabian oryx from the deserts of central Arabia. These hardy mammals are desert specialists, roaming over the barren landscape at night in search of patches of vegetation on which to graze. These animals used to range across the Arabian Peninsula until the end of the Second World War, when overhunting decimated the population, leading to the extinction of Arabian oryx in the wild. A careful captive breeding program has saved the species from total extinction and a few hundred individuals continue to survive in the wild.

The Arabian oryx is able to detect rainfall over great distances and moves towards it to take advantage of the vegetation that springs up after a rain event.

There are 26 species of goat antelopes divided in three groups, called tribes. The Ovibovini tribe contains the musk ox and the large, cattle-like takin from the highlands of China and Myanmar (Burma). The stocky bodies and thick fur of these animals insulate them from the cold. The tribe Rupicaprini consists largely of mountain-dwelling species, such as the chamois. This agile species is well suited to life on the narrow, icy ledges. All the remaining species belong to the Caprini tribe, which includes the domestic goat and sheep. Wild goats and sheep are hardy animals, but they face a significant threat from their domestic cousins. Huge herds of domestic goats and sheep strip the land of plant food, which drives wild species into more remote habitats. The domestic animals also spread disease and parasites among the wild species, which can decimate the population. Humans are also to blame for the decline in numbers. Some people rely on these animals for meat, but game hunters kill them for sport. Unlike many antelope species, wild goat antelopes will probably survive these threats. However, the population of some species has declined so much that they are listed as vulnerable by conservation organizations.

the females visit to mate, often with more than one male. Depending on variations in habitat, some grazing antelope breed all year round, while others have defined breeding seasons.

Goat antelopes

The wild relatives of goats and sheep are some of the hardiest animals on the planet. These animals live in some of the most inhospitable environments on Earth, ranging from the scorching desert to steep mountain tops.

Goats and sheep form a subgroup within the cattle family, known as the goat antelopes (subfamily Caprinae). Goat antelopes include an interesting variety of species. The largest, the musk ox, looks more like its wild cattle relatives than goats or sheep. Other species, such as the sure-footed chamois, are much smaller and look like grazing antelopes.

▶ *The woolly coat of the mountain goat insulates this hoofed mammal as it roams among the ice and snow of its mountain habitat.*

BATS

Bats are amazing flying mammals. Most species are nocturnal and emerge at night to feed on fruit or insects. Some bats navigate in complete darkness using a sophisticated system called echolocation.

There are more than 1,000 different kinds of bats, which makes up around 20 per cent of all the known mammal species. The smallest species, Kitti's hog-nosed bat, weighs about 2 g (0.07 oz) and is a few centimeters long. The largest species, the Malaysian flying fox, has a wingspan of 1.5 m (5 ft) and weighs 1.5 kg (3.3 lb).

Flying mammals

Bats are the only mammals that can fly. Other mammals, such as flying squirrels and colugos, glide and then only for short distances. Bats can fly because their front limbs have been modified into wings. (The family name for bats is Chiroptera, which comes from the Greek *kheiro* and *pteron*, meaning 'hand wings.') The wings are formed from a membrane of skin, called the patagium, which stretches between the four long fingers of each limb and the side of the bat's body. Bats do not flap their entire wings like birds; instead, they flap the long fingers that form the framework for the wings. This provides the lift force to fly around obstacles and chase down prey.

Bat groups

There are two main groups of bats – the megabats and the microbats. As their name suggests, megabats are mostly larger species that feed mostly on fruit, but also nectar and pollen. For this reason, they are also known as fruit bats. Megabats are also known as flying foxes because their large eyes, pointed ears and long snouts make them look like foxes. Megabats live in tropical rainforests, where they feed on the plentiful supply of fruit.

◄ *A spectacled flying fox hangs from the branch of a fig tree in Daintree National Park, Australia.*

Most microbats are much smaller than fruit bats. Most species hunt insects, although some larger species will eat small fish, frogs or lizards. Three bat species, the aptly named vampire bats, feed on the blood of other animals, including humans. Microbats have small eyes and rely on echolocation to find food. Although their eyesight is not as well developed as that of megabats, their vision is especially sensitive to low light situations.

Echolocation

Most microbats have very small eyes so they need another sense to fly and locate prey in complete darkness. Instead, they rely on a technique called echolocation, which means they can 'see with sound.' As bats fly, they emit a series of clicks. The clicks are high-pitched ultrasound waves that bounce off objects such as the side of a cave wall, or prey, such as a moth. The bat detects the sound reflections, or echoes, to find its way around, or home in on its prey. A bat chasing a moth will listen for the echoes getting closer together as it approaches, eventually homing in and snatching up its victim. Microbats have special body features to help detect the echoes. Some have long, pointed ears, which channel sound waves. Others have a growth called a nose leaf on the face, which helps to focus sound.

Feeding on fruits and flowers

Many bats feed on fruit, not only megabats but also a few species of microbats. Bats pluck fruit off trees using their teeth and fly back to their roosts to feed. The bats consume the sweet, fleshy parts of the fruit and discard the seeds and pulp by spitting them out onto the ground below. Some of the seeds may grow into new fruit trees. More than 150 plants rely on fruit-eating bats to help spread the seeds and colonize new areas.

Some bats prefer to drink the nectar inside flowers than eat fruit. Nectar-feeding bats usually have long snouts and tongues to lap up the sugary nectar. At the same time, pollen from the flower sticks to the bat's fur, which is transferred to another plant when the bat next stops to feed.

▼ *The enormous ears of the brown long-eared bat make this species easy to identify.*

Breeding and reproduction

Bats have many different reproductive strategies. A few species, such as the common vampire bat, breed many times each year. Most bats have a defined breeding season – usually in the spring in temperate climates, when food is most abundant. Females give birth to between one and three litters in each breeding season.

Bats have developed strategies to ensure that the reproductive cycle occurs at the best time for rearing young, for example, when most food is available. The females of some species store sperm in their bodies – mating may occur in the fall and fertilization is delayed until the following spring. The females of other species have delayed implantation, when the male's sperm fertilizes the egg, but the egg does not implant in the uterus until the conditions are ideal for raising young. Still other species, such as the Jamaican fruit-eating bat, exhibit diapause, which means the egg is fertilized and implants in the uterus, but development is delayed until the conditions are right. All of these adaptations result in the offspring being born when food – either fruit or insects – is in plentiful supply.

In most cases, the litter is limited to one young since the female must fly while she is pregnant. After birth, the females nurse their offspring until they are almost fully developed adults (the exact length of maternal care varies between species). Free-tailed bats rear their young in huge nurseries – often numbering more than 20 million individuals in one cave. No other mammal groups together in such large numbers. The mother usually gives parental care, although in some cases, individuals other than the female can help to raise the young. For example, female evening bats sometimes suckle offspring other than their own. While no one knows for sure why this behavior occurs, female bats usually return to their natal colony so it is likely that the females share a common ancestry. This helps ensure the survival of the next generation.

Bats at risk

Many species of bats are at risk. In tropical regions, farmers are clearing the forests for agricultural land and wiping out populations of flying foxes at the same time. Bats are also seen as pests in many countries since they eat such large quantities of fruit. Some farmers have fumigated roost sites to kill off bat numbers and protect their crops. Many people associate bats with negative images, including bloodsucking vampires and vectors for disease. Thankfully for bats, their public image is now improving. Conservation efforts are beginning to help improve the chances of their success.

Coming home to roost

Most bats are nocturnal animals and roost in large colonies during the day. Gathering together in large numbers (often more than one million individuals) provides warmth and protection against predators. Bats roost in many different places, ranging from large caves and tree crevices to man-made structures such as mines and buildings. A few species roost out in the open in trees, but this leaves them more open to predators. As a result, some of these species have stripes of color on their bodies to break up their outline, making them more difficult to spot.

▶ *A colony of greater horseshoe bats hibernate in a cave in Normandy, France.*

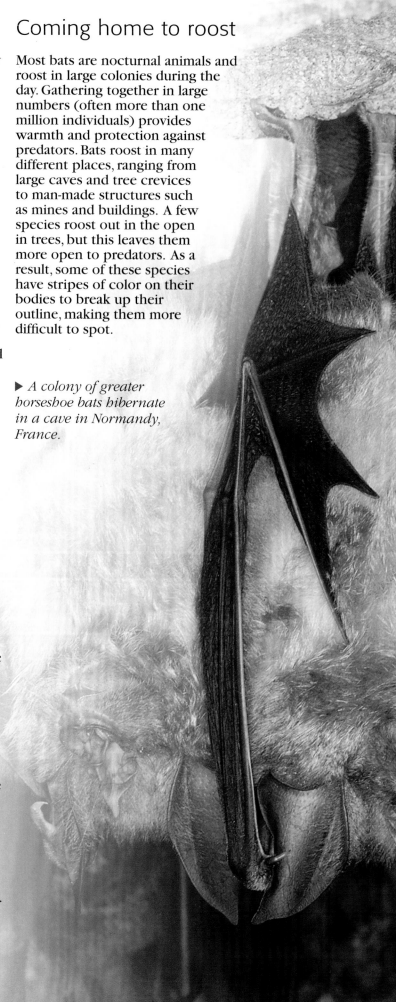

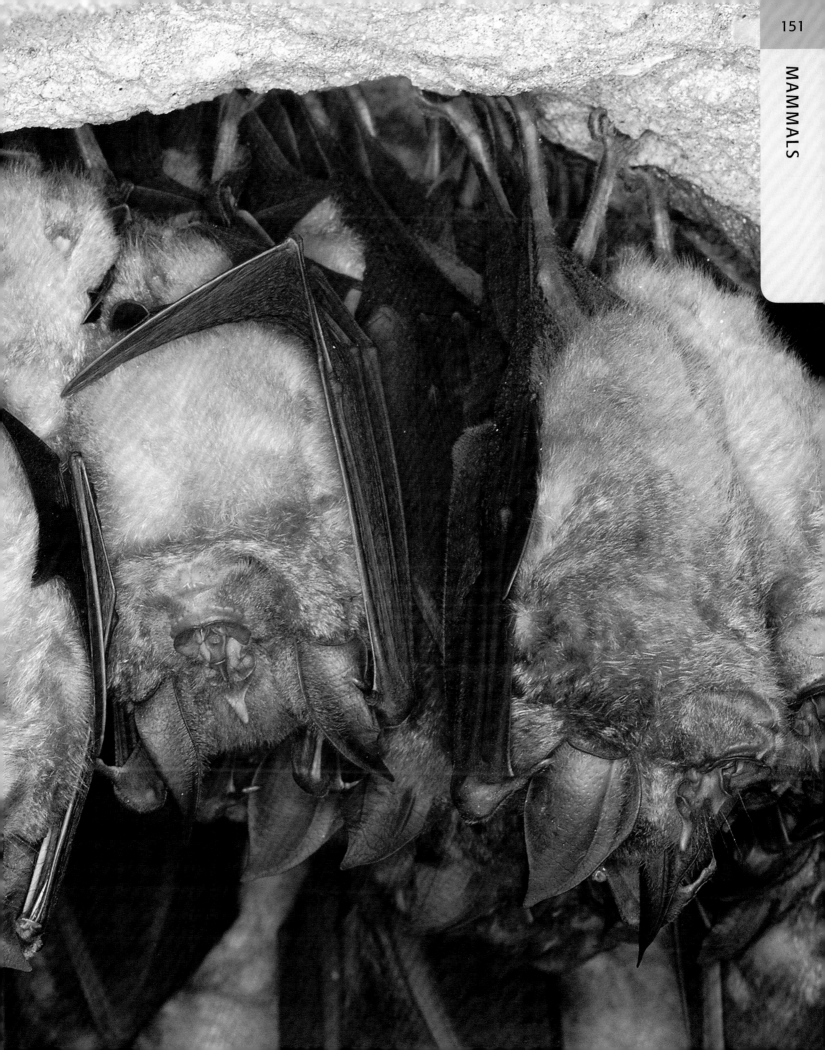

BEARS

The bear family contains just eight species, including some of the largest land-living carnivores on Earth. The group also includes the bamboo-eating giant panda, which is one of the rarest and most endangered animals in the world.

Watch a polar bear kill a seal and there is little doubt that these creatures are formidable hunters. Bears do attack people, but they are not as aggressive as most people think. Most bears avoid contact with people and will only attack when startled, or if they have cubs. Polar bears, perhaps the most dangerous species, will only attack in extreme hunger. Most people who live near polar bears carry guns, so it's usually the bear that ends up dead during a confrontation.

▼ *A brown bear fishes for salmon in a river in Alaska.*

Feeding habits

Bears are considered to be ferocious predators, but only the polar bear is particularly carnivorous, hunting seals, young walrus and young beluga whales. Most bears eat a wide range of food – berries and nuts in plentiful supply, as well as buds, leaves and tubers. Bears eat meat, fish and other animal food whenever the opportunity arises – brown bears will happily eat prey as diverse as salmon and squirrels, while the sun bear often breaks open termite mounds, using its long tongue to lick up the insect inhabitants. The giant panda is unusual in that it feeds almost exclusively on bamboo.

Classification

FAMILY	FELIDAE
GENUS	*PANTHERA*

Tiger	Species: *tigris* 6 subspecies
Lion	Species: *leo* 8 subspecies
Leopard	Species: *pardus* 9 subspecies
Jaguar	Species: *onca* 9 subspecies

Lion's share

The male moves in as soon as the lionesses have made a kill. The male is in charge of the pride and although he hasn't helped out in the hunt, he is responsible for defending the pride's territory. The male does this by roaring, pacing around and spraying urine on trees as a warning to male lions that wander by. The dominant male is usually a lion with a bit of life experience; younger males often group together and wait until they are ready to vie for leadership of the pride, challenging the dominant male in a fight that may ultimately end in death.

Solitary tigers

In stark contrast to the sociable lion, tigers are solitary big cats. These deadly predators are the largest of all the big cats, measuring up to 3.3 m (11 ft) long and weighing up to 300 kg (661 lb). They range from the Siberian taiga to the grasslands and tropical mangrove swamps of eastern and southern Asia.

With their stripy black and gold fur, tigers are the most recognizable of the big cats. Most hunt at night, but the stripy coat provides an effective camouflage against the grassy vegetation during the day, too.

Tiger tiger

There are many different subspecies of tigers, depending on where they live. The Bengal tiger (*Panthera tigris tigris*) is native to India and Bangladesh and is threatened with extinction, such is the decline in population in recent decades. Despite conservation efforts, poaching is still a widespread problem and there is no guarantee that the Bengal tiger can survive the threat. The Indochinese tiger (*Panthera tigris corbetti*) from Southeast Asia is also facing

extinction thanks to poaching and habitat loss and zoologists estimate that there are only a few hundred individuals left in the wild. The Malayan tiger (*Panthera tigris jacksoni*) has only been classified as a separate species since 2004. The population of tigers on the Malay peninsula is not as endangered as elsewhere, but still only numbers between 600 and 800 individuals. The Sumatran tiger (*Panthera tigris sumatrae*) is critically endangered and will undoubtedly become extinct if the destruction of prime rainforest habitat does not stop. The tigers are protected in national parks, but poaching is an ever-present danger. Likewise for the Siberian tiger (*Panthera tigris altaica*), which numbers fewer than 500 individuals. The last group, the South China tiger (*Panthera tigris amoyensis*), is one of the most critically endangered animals on the planet. In fact, the last sighting in the range, back in 2007, is disputed and these tigers may only exist as a captive subspecies.

Spotted cat

The distinctive spotted coat of the leopard (*Panthera pardus*) makes this big cat instantly recognizable. These efficient hunters are less endangered than other members of the cat family, thanks in large part to their adaptability in hunting and ability to climb trees. Most leopards are found in sub-Saharan Africa, but other populations exist in Pakistan, India, China and Malaysia.

▼ *An African leopard cub rests on tree branches in the Serengeti National Park, Tanzania.*

The leopard's success (compared to other big cats) lies in its opportunistic feeding behavior. Leopards will eat anything from dung beetles to gazelles and these nocturnal predators are very swift and agile, sprinting at more than 55 km (34 mi) an hour and leaping up to 3 m (10 ft) into the air. After the kill, leopards often drag their meal up into the treetops, carrying up to three times their own weight. This means the leopard is less likely to lose its kill to scavengers.

Color change

Black panther is the name given to a black color variant of the jaguar in South America and of the leopard in Africa and Asia. The black panther is exactly the same species, but the natural spotted pattern is masked by a genetic difference that produces an excess of black pigment, called melanin, in the skin.

▶ *Black panthers are melanistic color variants in several species of larger cats.*

Big cat, big bite

The jaguar (*Panthera onca*) is the only big cat native to the Americas. This spotted cat closely resembles its cousin, the leopard, but it is bulkier and more closely resembles the tiger in behavior. The jaguar's range extends from southern Mexico south to Paraguay and Argentina. These solitary predators lie in ambush in the dense vegetation of the tropical rainforest, hoping to pounce on a passing deer or tapir. Such is the power of the jaguar's jaws that it can pierce the armored shell of an armadillo and it has even been known to tackle predators, such as anacondas and caimans.

Jaguars have no natural predators in the wild, but numbers are still declining because human activities are destroying their habitat. Jaguars are also seen as pests by farmers raising cattle and they are often simply shot on sight, despite being protected by international laws.

Other 'big cats'

Three other cat species do not fall into the big cat category but are equally worthy candidates. They are the cheetah, snow leopard and the clouded leopard. With its loose and rangy body and long limbs, the cheetah is built for speed. These large cats are usually found on the African savanna, but a few critically endangered Asiatic cheetahs also exist in the Middle East. Cheetahs are swift predators and can sprint in short bursts of up to 100 km (62 mi) per hour, chasing fast-moving prey such as gazelles and other antelopes. Unlike the true big cats, the claws of the cheetah are straight and blunt and cannot fully retract, which gives these formidable predators grip as they twist and turn after

their prey. The average chase lasts for up to a minute. About 50 per cent of all chases are successful and the cheetah kills its victim with a suffocating bite to the neck. Adults may kill every few days to sustain good health, but females with cubs need to kill every day to feed the young. Many cubs die through starvation and many others fall victim to larger predators, such as lions.

The snow leopard is another large cat that lives in the high mountains of central Asia, predominantly in China. These endangered animals are well suited to life in the mountains, with thick fur and long tails to help them balance on narrow, icy ledges. Snow leopards prey on a range of animals, including deer and goats and young horses and yak. Smaller prey, such as hares and marmots, are also taken in the summer months. Snow leopards stalk their prey, coming within 40 m (131 ft) or closer before emerging to quickly chase down their victims.

The clouded leopard is a lesser-known species from the tropical and subtropical rainforests of central and Southeast Asia. Clouded leopards are thought to hunt small mammals, such as wild pigs, but they may also take prey, such as monkeys, birds and domestic chickens and goats. Like so many wild cats, the clouded leopard is threatened by habitat destruction as farmers clear the land to grow crops. Similarly, the population of clouded leopards has also suffered thanks to hunting.

Small cats

The remaining members of the cat family are grouped together as 'small cats' from the genus (group) *Felis*. These cats resemble the familiar domestic cat both in appearance and behavior, although the term 'small cat' again is rather misleading since the puma can grow to be much bigger than the leopard. Almost all small cat species are solitary hunters, and they occupy a wide range of habitats. The aptly named sand cat lives in the deserts of Africa and Asia, for example, while the secretive margay hunts birds and small mammals in the forests and scrubland of Central and South America. When small cats are found living near human settlements, they will often prey on domesticated animals.

◀ *The snow leopard is native to the highlands of Central Asia, where it hunts large mammals, such as ass and yak.*

▶ *The ocelot is a small wildcat that lives in the rainforests of Central and South America.*

Protecting small cats

Many small cats are so vulnerable that international laws have been established to protect them. The international fur market is no longer as popular as it was in the middle of the 20th century, but trophy hunters and farmers continue to kill small cats in large numbers. However, habitat destruction remains the biggest problem facing wild cats around the world. The news is not all bad, however. Conservation efforts are starting to increase the population of small cats in some areas, particularly North America, where species, such as the lynx and puma are beginning to recover.

Small cat classification

The 30 species of living small cats are split into lineages (groups) of related species. They are:

Asian small cat lineage	Bay cat lineage	Wild cat lineage	Lynx lineage	American spotted cat lineage	Puma lineage
Fishing cat	Asian golden cat	Black-footed cat	Bobcat	Geoffroy's cat	Jaguarundi
Flat-headed cat	Bay cat	Chinese desert cat	Canadian lynx	Kodkod	Puma
Iriomote cat		Jungle cat	Iberian lynx	Margay cat	
Leopard cat	**Caracal lineage**	Pallas's cat	Lynx	Andean mountain cat	**Others**
Rusty-spotted cat	Caracal	Sand cat		Ocelot	African golden cat
		Wildcat		Pampas cat	Marbled cat
				Tiger cat	Serval

CIVETS AND RELATIVES

Civets and their relatives are catlike carnivores that live mainly in trees, although some species live in underground burrows. Most species are secretive, solitary hunters, but a few forage in large troops of up to 20 individuals.

Civets and their relatives share the same basic body plan, with slender, muscular bodies, short legs and long tails. Most species have thick fur, which may be marked with spots and stripes. Scent glands under the tails of civets and genets secrete a noxious chemical, which is used to deter predators. Many mongooses rely on social groups as defense against predators.

Civets and genets

Civets and genets belong to a diverse family of catlike predators (*Viverridae*). While many species are very different in form and behavior, they share many characteristics. For example, most species are solitary and nocturnal. During the day, they rest in rock crevices, empty burrows, or tree hollows. At night, they emerge to forage on bulbs, fruit and nuts, or ambush prey, such as insects, small reptiles, birds and mammals. Civets and genets are found from southern Europe and sub-Saharan Africa to central and Southeast Asia. Most live in the treetops of tropical rainforests. The population of many species is declining thanks to activities such as clearing land for growing crops or cattle ranching.

▼ *A fossa forages in the leaf litter. This large catlike predator is the largest carnivore in Madagascar.*

Fossas

One of the most fascinating species in this group is the fossa (*Eupleridae*), which lives in the tropical forests of Madagascar off the southeast coast of Africa. Lemurs are the main source of food for the fossa, but they also prey on lizards and game-fowl. Fossas are also unusual in their mating behavior. Females establish mating sites and pair with as many males as they can before giving up the site to a new female, who repeats the behavior. By mating with several males, some biologists think that the different sperm compete to fertilize the egg. Only the strongest sperm (from the strongest male) survives to pass on characteristics to the next generation.

The mongoose family

Unlike the mainly solitary civets and genets, many members of the mongoose family (*Herpestidae*) – such as meerkats and banded mongooses – are social animals that live in large troops. Social species usually live in open habitats, such as grasslands and hunt insects and small vertebrates during the day. Some are so fast and agile that they can even tackle venomous snakes, such as cobras. Solitary mongooses usually live in trees in forests and woodlands and hunt large prey at night.

Living in a group offers protection against predators, such as birds of prey, snakes and large carnivores, such as jackals. When the group is foraging on the ground for insects, one mongoose usually climbs to a vantage point and acts as a lookout. If the lookout spots a predator, it cries out with a loud alarm call and the troop will scatter for cover. In fact, there are different alarm calls for different predators to give the troop the best chance of escape. There is little time to react to a

▲ *The Malagasy, or striped, civet forages for food in the forests of eastern Madagascar.*

bird of prey swooping down from the sky, so on hearing a call that indicates a bird of prey, each mongoose will sprint flat out for the nearest hole. If the call indicates a terrestrial predator, such as a jackal, the mongoose still dashes for cover but has more time to pick a route to best avoid the attacker.

Banded mongooses sometimes employ a 'mutual defense' strategy against predators, such as jackals. Members of the troop move toward the predator as a tightly knit group. The strategy usually pays off, since most predators will avoid what appears to be one large animal moving menacingly toward them.

▶ *A meerkat stands on guard looking out for predators while other members of the colony search for food.*

DEER

Deer include around 40 species of hoofed, plant-eating mammals that are found in many different habitats around the world. The striking antlers of male deer are what distinguish this group from similar hoofed mammals, such as the antelopes.

Deer are found in a wide range of habitats. Most species prefer to hide away in the dense vegetation of forests and woodlands, but some roam the Arctic tundra and windswept grasslands of Asia and the Americas. Deer come in many different shapes and sizes, but most have a barrel-shaped body, long neck, large eyes on the sides of the head and pointed ears – all adaptations to help spot the many predators that hunt these animals. The fur of these animals is often brown and dappled, or spotted, which acts as camouflage.

Deer relations

Deer are part of the larger group of even-toed ungulates (hoofed mammals) – two toes support their weight. A scent gland between the toes leaves a trail on the ground as a marker for other deer to follow. Other even-toed ungulates include camels, hippos and wild pigs, but the deer's closest relations are the antelopes and wild cattle. These mammals are called ruminants, which means they have an unusual habit of chewing the cud. They regurgitate plant food, chewing the tough fibers several times before digesting them in their many-chambered stomachs.

▶ *Reindeer graze on mosses, lichens and fungi during the harsh winter months, when other plant food is scarce.*

Different groups

There are three main families of deer. True deer belong to the family Cervidae, which includes familiar species, such as the elk (or moose) and reindeer (or caribou). True deer can be further subdivided into two groups based on their geographical distribution. Elk and reindeer belong to the New World species, which originated in the Americas. Old World species include the fallow deer, red deer and lesser-known deer such as the small and secretive muntjac. All these species originated in Europe and Asia. The distinction between Old World and New World deer is now largely a reflection of the ancestry of these animals, since many species have been introduced to different parts of the world.

The other two main deer families are the musk deer (Moschidae) and the chevrotains, or mouse deer (Tragulidae). There are seven species of musk deer that live in forests and woodland across Asia. Most species are facing extinction because they are hunted for their musk. Males secrete this pungent substance to attract females during the breeding season and it has become a popular ingredient in perfumes. The four species of chevrotains are also known as mouse deer because of their timid appearance. They live in the rainforests of Africa and Asia.

Antlers

The most striking feature of the true deer is the antlers. The antlers are made of solid bone and project from the skull of the males. Reindeer (or caribou) are the only species where females also have antlers, but these are normally smaller than those of their male counterparts. In the spring, when the antlers first appear, they are covered with a sensitive skin called velvet. As the antlers grow larger and larger, the velvet gradually dries up and cracks. The males then start to rub off the velvet against trees and shrubs. By the fall, the antlers are fully grown.

Male deer are now ready for the rut at the start of the breeding season. The rut is when male deer compete with each other for the right to mate with the females. Males engage in ritual displays, showing off their strength and roaring at each other. In many cases, the weaker male backs down without a fight. If the two males are evenly matched, however, they will usually lock antlers and fight. The winner earns the right to mate with the females and pass his genes on to the next generation of deer.

The antlers are shed after the rut in the fall, but the growing cycle continues the next year. The antlers usually grow back larger each year, which reflects the age and experience of the male. Growing antlers comes at a considerable cost to the males. The antlers of the largest living species, the European elk (or moose), weigh in excess of 30 kg (66 lb) and it uses up a lot of energy to grow and then shed these bony projections year after year.

Unlike the true deer, musk deer and the chevrotains have long upper canine teeth instead of antlers. These teeth project below the lower jaws of the males and are used as weapons to establish dominance.

Solitary or social

Whether a deer chooses to lead a solitary lifestyle or live in a group largely depends on the availability of food. Browsers are more selective and there is more competition for resources and so these animals usually live

▼ *The lesser mouse deer is the smallest known hoofed mammal, standing at less than 45 cm (18 in) tall.*

▲ *Two young red deer stags lock horns during the rut.*

alone or in small groups. Browsing deer usually live in dense forests and woodland, so there is much better cover in which to hide from predators.

Grazers usually live out in the open where food is plentiful and so these animals usually live in groups. Outside the breeding season, the groups usually consist of deer of the same sex. Since grazing deer roam open habitats, living in a group offers protection from predators. Many large carnivores rely on deer as a source of food and the predator and prey are locked in an ongoing battle for survival. Some species rely on speed and endurance to escape, while others sprint away and hide in dense vegetation.

People pressure

Deer have a long association with people. People have domesticated certain deer species. In the past, people tamed large deer, such as the moose, as a beast of burden. The Sami people still herd reindeer across the frozen landscape of Northern Europe. Deer farming is popular in China and several species are thriving, including the red deer and sika deer. While deer farming preserves the population

of deer, it is generally bad for wild animals since the farmed animals spread disease and can decimate wild populations. In the wild, deer face the usual threats of habitat destruction and overhunting. Many species are big game animals, although hunting is now seasonal in most countries. The red deer and roe deer are highly prized trophies in Europe, while the white-tailed deer and mule deer are important game animals in North America.

▶ *An adult elk (or moose as it is known in North America) feeds on submerged plants in a lake in Alaska.*

DOGS

Members of the dog family, or canids, include coyotes, foxes, jackals, wolves and wild dogs, as well as the dogs humans keep as pets. Wild dogs are highly efficient predators, with keen senses and endurance to track down and chase their prey and sharp canine teeth for killing their quarry.

The dog family (Canidae) includes 35 different species that share the same basic body plan. Wild dogs have lithe bodies, deep chests, long legs and long, bushy tails. The paws have hard pads and blunt claws for gripping the ground. This body plan has given dogs great strength and stamina, which comes into good effect when they chase prey. Dogs have extremely keen senses to track their prey. Packed with olfactory organs, the long, pointed muzzle is the main sense organ, but hearing is especially acute and eyesight is also well developed.

In the wild, dogs are usually found in open grassland habitats throughout the world. Wild dogs inhabit every major continent but are notably absent from islands, such as Madagascar – although domestic dogs have a worldwide distribution. The dingo from Australia is usually considered to be a wild dog, although it actually originates from domestic stock that was introduced to the country about 4,000 years ago.

◄ *The gray wolf is the largest wild member of the dog family and the ancestor of all domestic dog breeds.*

▲ *Dingoes are the descendants of domestic dogs that escaped into the Australian wilderness thousands of years ago.*

Pack of dogs

Smaller dogs, such as foxes and jackals, usually live alone or in pairs depending on the availability of food. All large dogs live in complex social groups called packs. Each pack consists of a dominant male and female – the only individuals that mate – and younger individuals of different ages. Young dogs usually stay with their parents for several years and may help to raise their siblings. The pack defends the resources within its territory, marking the boundaries with urine.

Living in a pack is extremely beneficial when hunting prey. It offers individual dogs the chance to hunt prey much larger than they could manage on their own. The usual strategy is to track a herd of antelope or deer and then work together to pick off one weaker or young individual. The pack then slowly runs the animal down until it eventually collapses from exhaustion. The dogs then move in for the kill. Dogs have long, fang-like canine teeth to stab and kill their prey and slashing carnassials to slice through the flesh. The pack will eat as much meat as it can at the site of the kill. Adults regurgitate meat for the cubs back at the den.

Building bonds

Living in a pack means that it is important for dogs to build and maintain close bonds with each other. Dogs do this in many ways, for example, by grooming, licking and whining pack members. Lower ranking dogs wait behind the dominant pair to feed after a kill and show signs of submission by holding the ears back, crouching low to the ground and holding the tail between the legs. As the breeding season approaches, pack tension increases as individuals jostle for the right to mate. Younger dogs may challenge the dominant pair and fights break out among lower ranking dogs to move up the pack hierarchy. Eventually, the dominant pair mates and calm is restored within the pack. At this point, when the hierarchy has been established for the next few months, some of the lower ranking dogs may decide to leave and start a pack of their own.

Different dogs

There are three main groups, or genera, of dogs. Members of the genus *Canis* include the coyote, dingo, three species of wolves and three species of jackals.

▲ *The spines of the short-nosed echidna protect it from predators, such as dingoes.*

Venomous mammals

Another unusual feature of monotremes is their ability to produce venom – some shrew species are the only other mammals that possess this ability. Echidnas produce venom, but the gland and duct do not develop fully for the animal to effectively deliver the venom. However, the male platypus makes full use of this formidable weapon. The venom gland leads to a horny spur on the platypus's ankle and the male jabs it into his attacker's body to inject the venom. The venom is potent enough to kill a dog and in humans it attacks pain receptors in the skin, causing intense pain and inflammation. No one knows for sure why the monotremes have venom glands. Some zoologists suggest that it helps males define territories during the breeding season, while others think that it developed as a form of defense against a predator that has long since become extinct.

Breeding behavior

All monotremes are solitary animals, but males and females pair up to mate during loosely defined breeding seasons. Once mating has occurred, females lay soft-shelled eggs that hatch within around ten days. Like all mammals, female monotremes feed their young with milk produced by mammary glands, though the milk is secreted through openings in the skin, as monotremes lack defined nipples. The platypus keeps her young in special breeding burrows until they are ready to emerge three or four months later – usually in the Australian summer months (January to March) when aquatic invertebrates are in plentiful supply.

Echidnas lay eggs in the same way, but the incubation takes place in a pouch on the mother's body. The mother keeps her young in the pouch after it hatches and it suckles on its mother's milk for around six months. For the next six months, the young is raised in a nursery burrow. After a year, the young becomes an adult and starts to fend for itself.

ELEPHANTS

◄ *A herd of African elephants cross the dry savanna in Botswana.*

Elephants are the largest of all the mammals that live on land. These giants live in the grasslands and rainforests of sub-Saharan Africa and South and Southeast Asia.

The elephant family consists of three different species. The African bush elephant roams the African savanna and is the biggest of the three species. The males, or bulls, can stand up to 4 m (13 ft) tall and weigh between 6,000 kg (13,000 lb) and 9,000 kg (20,000 lb). The African forest elephant is found in the rainforests of Central and West Africa. These elephants are much smaller than their savanna relatives – adults stand at 2.5 m (8 ft) and weigh around 2,700 kg (6,000 lb) at most. The Asian elephant lives in the dense lowland jungle of South and Southeast Asia. In terms of size and weight, the Asian elephant lies somewhere in between its two African cousins.

Elephant anatomy

All elephants share the same basic body plan. These mammals have large, barrel-shaped bodies with a distinctive downward-curving (convex) spine. Four pillar-like legs support the elephant's heavy head and giant frame. All elephants have large flapping ears, but the ears of the two African species are much larger than those of their Asian counterpart. A network of blood vessels in the ears radiates heat away from the body, helping to keep elephants cool in hot and humid conditions where they live.

◀ A male African elephant, or bull, has large, curved tusks, which are elongated incisor teeth.

Perhaps the most distinctive characteristic of an elephant's body is its long trunk. The trunk is a long extension of the animal's upper lip and nose. The elephant's muscular trunk is extremely flexible. Elephants use them to perform a wide range of tasks, such as lifting heavy logs and plucking leaves from the tallest branches. The elephant also uses its trunk as a hose to squirt water (and dust) over its body.

The tip of the Asian elephant's trunk is slightly different to those of the African species. In Asian elephants, the trunk ends with a single finger-like projection, called a process. African elephants have two processes on the end of their trunks. The processes are highly mobile and are used to pick up small objects.

Another distinctive feature of the elephant's body are the long, curved tusks. The tusks are elongations of the elephant's incisor teeth. The tusks of the bulls are longer and thicker than those of the females, or cows. The tusks of Asian elephants are smaller still and in cows, are hidden by the lip.

Feeding habits

Elephants eat a lot of food to support their enormous bulk. An adult bull needs about 160 kg (353 lb) of food every day. Elephants use their muscular trunks to pull down branches and then pick off the foliage with great dexterity using the processes at the tips of their trunks. Elephants eat a wide range of plant material, from bark and branches to grasses, leaves, green shoots and, occasionally, fruit in the case of the African forest elephant. Elephants have large, ridged molars and premolars to grind up all this coarse plant material. As they feed, elephants cause a huge amount of damage to the environment, stripping bark, breaking branches and even uprooting small trees. In areas where there are large herds of elephants, the habitat often changes dramatically as elephants eat their way through the dense vegetation, leaving behind open grassland.

One unusual feeding habit of elephants is the way they supplement their diet by eating salt. Elephants often visit areas of salt-rich soil, breaking up the salt crystals with their long tusks. The location of these salt sites seems to pass through the generations as young elephants learn from older members of the herd.

Social structure

Elephants live in groups called herds, which consist of a dominant (usually the oldest) female, called the matriarch and young female relatives and their offspring. In areas of dense vegetation, different herds of African elephants often join together to form large groups containing 100 or more individuals. Communication is very important among members of the herd. Elephants call to each other and stamp their feet to communicate and they also cooperate, for example, when one member of the herd stands as a lookout while the other elephants take dust baths.

The sense of touch seems to play an important part in elephant communication. Elephants greet each other by standing close and intertwining their trunks and females are rarely more than a trunk's length away from their young, called calves. In any case, every member of the herd is on hand to share the responsibility for protecting the young elephants from predators, such as lions. Since all the females in a herd are usually related, there is some genetic benefit to this shared responsibility.

Most of the time, the bulls live separately from the cows. Older bulls usually live alone, while younger males form small 'bachelor herds.' The bulls join the herd to breed but share no part in raising their offspring.

Elephants at risk

Elephants enjoy a mixed relationship with people. In Asia, people have harnessed the power of elephants and used them as draft animals to move heavy objects,

Elderly elephants

Elephants are some of the longest-lived mammals. In the wild, elephants live for about 60 years on average; humans are the only other mammals that live longer. Elephants, especially the bulls, grow in size throughout their long lives, and there is a considerable difference in size between an elderly bull and a young male.

such as logs. But human activities, such as forest clearance and hunting, have also decimated the elephant population in some parts of the world. The International Union for Conservation of Nature (IUCN) lists the African elephant as vulnerable and the Asian elephant as endangered. Zoologists think that there are fewer than 55,000 Asian elephants in the world, including those in captivity.

The biggest impact on elephant numbers has been hunting. In the past, many people hunted elephants for their tusks, which are prized as a source of ivory. Since the reproductive rate of elephants is so slow, it takes a long time for numbers to recover. Many countries have passed laws to protect elephants, but there is still a demand for ivory and the hunting continues.

▼ *A pair of African elephants take a dust bath. This protects the elephants from insect bites and keeps the skin in good condition.*

GIRAFFE AND OKAPI

As the world's tallest animal, the giraffe needs little introduction. However, the giraffe's close relative, the okapi, is much less well known. Both species live in Africa, but each one exploits different habitats and leads very different lifestyles.

▲ *Standing at more than 5 m (16 ft) tall, the giraffe is the tallest of all the mammals.*

The giraffe is one of the most instantly recognizable animals on the planet. These sociable mammals roam the open woodlands and savanna of Africa in small herds. Males stand at more than 5 m (16 ft) tall – most of this height is down to their long necks. Males use their necks in a suitably named display called 'necking,' when they lock necks to display their strength to the females. The giraffe's head has small horns, called ossicones, which are covered with skin but are hard

enough to cause damage when males clash heads during these fights. The winner of these 'contests of strength' earns the right to mate with all the females (cows) in the herd.

The legs of the giraffe also make up a lot of the animal's height. The front legs are longer than the hind legs, so the giraffe splays them to stoop down and drink at a waterhole. However, this ungainly posture belies the strength of the giraffe's front legs. One kick is all that is needed to dispatch a predator, such as a lion.

Pros and cons

Since giraffes tower over all other African herbivores, they can feed on a wider range of vegetation. A simple evolutionary lesson explains why this might have been the case: over millions of years, giraffe-like ancestors competed for the same food. Some individuals grew taller to exploit the upper levels of vegetation. In times of shortage, these animals were less likely to starve and so taller individuals survived and passed on their "tall" genes to the next generation.

There are disadvantages to being so tall, however. One of the main problems is the pressure it places on the heart to pump blood all the way up to the brain. Giraffes have blood vessels in their neck to regulate blood pressure, as does the tight skin around the legs. This prevents blood accumulating in the lower regions of the giraffe's body. It acts a little like the 'anti-G suits' worn by fighter pilots to prevent them from blacking out in tight maneuvers.

Coat markings

The pattern of markings on the coats of giraffes may look the same to the untrained eye, but the markings change depending on the region in which the animal lives and also on its diet. Some giraffes have clear, tan markings, while others have black patches and blurry yellow patterns. These irregular blotches help to disguise the outline of the giraffe against the patchy trees and bushes of the African savanna. The markings are unique to giraffes and zoologists that study these animals often use the skin patterns to identify different individuals.

The okapi

With its distinctive stripy skin, from a distance the secretive okapi looks more like a zebra than a giraffe at first glance. Like the giraffe, the okapi has a long neck and reaches up to browse on the tallest juicy shoots, soft twigs and succulent leaves. Okapis also have skin-covered horns and dark tongues, which they use to gather plant food. Unlike the giraffe, however, the okapi

is a solitary animal that hides in the dense rainforests of central Africa. These animals are so secretive that no one even knew they existed before 1901.

▼ *The distinctive stripes on the rump of the okapi give this mammal its alternative name – the 'forest zebra.'*

HIPPOPOTAMUS

The hippopotamus is a large, semi-aquatic herbivore that lives along the rivers and lakes of sub-Saharan Africa. Its close relative, the pygmy hippopotamus, is much smaller and hides away in the dense forests and swamps of West Africa.

In a continent that boasts predators as fearsome as cobras and lions, it may be surprising to learn that the hippo is also one of Africa's deadliest animals. They are one of the largest African mammals. Adult males can reach up to 5 m (16 ft) long and weigh up to 4,500 kg (9,921 lb). Hippos have very short tempers, especially if they are protecting young hippos. An apparently docile hippo can suddenly turn into a lethal killing machine. These animals have two large, razor-sharp teeth on the lower jaw. These can reach up to 30 cm (12 in) in length above the gum line.

Keeping cool

Hippos spend most of the day wallowing in rivers and lakes. Unlike many other mammals, they cannot sweat, so life in the water keeps the hippos cool in the heat of the African savanna. Glands in the hippo's skin secrete a thick fluid that acts as a natural sunscreen, protecting the skin from the strong sunlight. At night, hippos emerge from the water to feed. Typically, a hippo wanders more than 5 km (3 mi) as it grazes on grasses and other plant material. Adults consume around 40 kg (88 lb) of plant matter on these nocturnal feeding expeditions.

▼ A male hippo gapes his mouth and bares his teeth in a display of dominance. Fights between males are common and may result in serious injuries.

Hybrid horses

Different members of the horse family can successfully interbreed. Pairing a male donkey and female horse results in a mule. Pairing a male horse and a female donkey produces a hinny. The bizarrely named zedonk is the result of a pairing between a male zebra and a female donkey. While all the offspring are born as healthy individuals, these hybrids cannot breed to produce offspring of their own.

Feeding habits

Members of the horse family are herbivores. The jaws are packed with hard-wearing cheek teeth (molars and premolars) to cut through grass. Horses mainly eat grass, although they may browse on bark, buds and leaves. Unlike members of the cattle family, horses do not ruminate. (This is when animals regurgitate plant food, chewing the tough fibers several times before digesting them in their many-chambered stomachs.) Instead, horses ferment the ground up plant matter in their hindgut. This allows them to eat more food, which passes through the digestive system much more quickly. As a result, members of the horse family can survive in deserts and other areas where the quality of vegetation is poor.

▶ *The African wild ass lives in the rocky deserts of Central Africa, where it feeds on almost any plant food it can find – from grasses to thorny acacia bushes.*

Solitary or social

Some members of the horse family live in social groups called herds, which are made up of one dominant male, called a stallion, which protects a group of females, or mares, and their offspring. The stallion defends his 'harem' of females from other males that may attempt to mate with the mares. The fights between stallions are often violent, with both horses rearing up and 'boxing' with their front legs, or kicking out with their rear legs. The loser is driven away and the winner stays to control the harem.

Wild asses and Grévy's zebra adopt a different strategy – stallions live alone and defend a territory instead of a group of mares. The stallion marks the boundaries of his territory with dung and drives away any other stallions that may wander passed, but he mates with any mares that pass through.

Horses and humans

The relationship between horses and humans goes back thousands of years. Wild asses were the first species to be domesticated in the Middle East, but they were gradually displaced by the swifter and stronger horses for many purposes. Today, horses are mainly used for travel and recreation, although the donkey is still an important beast of burden in many countries.

HYENAS

Hyenas are often mistaken for dogs but, in fact, they are closer relatives of cats and civets. Spotted hyenas are highly efficient predators and scavengers. They hunt in groups called clans and can take down large wildebeest. Spotted hyenas can also drive lions away from their kill.

Hyenas are a small group of carnivores that lives in the savanna, scrub and semi-desert habitats of Africa and parts of southern Asia. There are four species in the group: the brown hyena, spotted hyena, striped hyena and the aardwolf. All share the same basic body plan, with a large head, short muzzle and pointed ears. The most distinctive feature is the back, which slopes down from the base of the neck to the end of the bushy tail. This feature is due to the hyena's long front legs and short hind legs.

Feeding frenzy

Hyenas are formidable carnivores. They have powerful jaw muscles and strong teeth that can crunch through bones. The spotted hyena is a particularly efficient hunter and scavenger. Individuals will hunt small animals, such as hares and game birds, while the clan can bring down much larger prey, such as wildebeest and zebra and drive a pride of lions from their kill.

Spotted hyenas will consume almost every part of the carcass, including the skin and bones. They can eat a lot of meat – almost one-third of their own body weight in one sitting. The only parts of the kill the hyena cannot digest are the fur and hooves, so it regurgitates them as small pellets.

▼ *A pack of spotted hyenas feed on the remains of a wildebeest carcass.*

Living in groups

Brown hyenas and striped hyenas live in pairs or small groups and defend a territory from neighboring groups. They mark the boundaries of the territory with dung, urine and pungent secretions from a gland by the anus.

▶ *The hyena has a distinctive body shape – its back slopes gently downward from the shoulders to the tail.*

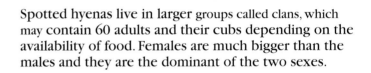

Spotted hyenas live in larger groups called clans, which may contain 60 adults and their cubs depending on the availability of food. Females are much bigger than the males and they are the dominant of the two sexes.

Spotted hyena cubs are reared in a communal den. Within the den, one cub dominates the milk supply. During lean times, when food is scarce and the mother's milk runs short, the dominant cub may kill its siblings to ensure survival. The cubs are weaned after around 16 months, when they are almost fully grown adults. Then they will accompany the clan on hunting expeditions.

The aardwolf

The aardwolf is unusual among the hyenas because it does not hunt large prey. Instead, it uses its long, sticky tongue to lick up termites, crushing them between its small, flat teeth. Aardwolves need to eat a few hundred thousand termites every day to sustain their weight, but they will supplement their diet with the occasional grub and other soft-bodied invertebrates.

The aardwolf is a nocturnal forager and rests in a burrow in the heat of the day. These animals are solitary, but the males and females pair up to breed. The female bears between two and four cubs after a gestation period of about 90 days. The cubs emerge from the burrow after about four weeks and are weaned after 16 weeks.

INSECT-EATING MAMMALS

Insect-eating mammals, or insectivores, feed mainly on insects, although many species eat other invertebrates, such as worms and spiders. There are many different groups of insectivores, including anteaters, hedgehogs, moles and shrews.

Insect-eating mammals come in many different shapes and sizes. In general, most species have small eyes and ears and long snouts, which give them a keen sense of smell to sniff out insect food. Body shape varies between different species. Moles have cylindrical bodies, which suits their burrowing lifestyle, while hedgehogs and tenrecs have short, squat bodies. Anteaters are much bigger than most other insectivores. These bizarre-looking creatures have long, tubular snouts that gradually widen out into a small

head. The armadillos are smaller than the anteaters, with smaller snouts. Armor-like plates of hardened skin cover the armadillo's body. This provides protection against predators.

The behavior and lifestyle of insect-eating mammals varies according to species. Most insectivores live on the land, but a few species, such as the tenrecs and water shrew, are semi-aquatic, which means they spend a lot of time in the water. Still others, such as moles, are burrowing animals and excavate complex underground tunnel systems.

Zoologists think that insectivores are some of the most primitive of all the mammals. They have kept many of the features of their ancestors, such as a small brain and primitive dentition (arrangement of teeth). Anteaters do not have any teeth at all.

▼ A brown-breasted hedgehog feeds on an earthworm. The sharp spines on the hedgehog's body protect it from predators, such as foxes.

Marsupial movements

All marsupials live on the land, and most species move by running across the ground on all four legs. Tree-dwelling marsupials such as the various possum species and the koala are excellent climbers. Some possums – the aptly named gliders – 'fly' between the treetops, using a flap of skin between the front and back legs as a parachute to slow their descent. Kangaroos and wallabies hop on their long back legs and feet. Hopping uses up a lot of energy when the kangaroo or wallaby moves slowly, but as the animal builds up speed, hopping becomes more energy efficient.

Raising young

Like almost all other mammals, marsupials give birth to live young and feed them with milk secreted by mammary glands on the female's body. Most mammals that bear live young do so after a long period of development inside the body of the female. During this period of gestation, the female nourishes the unborn offspring through a placenta, which is filled with blood and delivers oxygen and nutrients through the umbilical cord. The offspring of marsupials are born after a short gestation period.

Without a placenta to provide nourishment, the newborn marsupial needs to feed on its mother's milk to grow and develop. So the tiny newborn marsupial, which still resembles an embryo, crawls over its mother's fur in search of a nipple. The newborn latches on to the milk source and remains fixed to the nipple for several weeks or more. In most marsupials, the nipples are hidden beneath a pouch, which provides a safe home for the young. Large marsupials usually give birth to a single young, but smaller species may have litters of five or more offspring. The young marsupials eventually outgrow the pouch and become independent of their mother. How long this takes varies according to the different species.

Australian marsupials

The kangaroo and the koala are some of the most familiar of all the Australian marsupials. The largest marsupial of all is the red kangaroo, which roams over the open grasslands and deserts of Australia. Kangaroos time their reproduction to the availability of water – in times of plenty the population may reach up to 15 million, and they are regarded as pests. During a drought,

◀ *A female koala and her three-month-old joey sit in a tree, resting between meals of eucalyptus leaves.*

however, the population can dip to below 5 million. This is because male kangaroos do not produce sperm, so the females cannot conceive.

The koala spends almost all of its life in eucalyptus trees, feeding on the leaves. Koalas eat around 500 g (18 oz) of leaves every day to sustain their weight. In between meals, the koala sleeps and occasionally drops down on to the forest floor to eat soil and gravel. This helps the koala digest the tough and fibrous eucalyptus leaves.

The Tasmanian devil is a carnivore that lives on the island of Tasmania, southeast of mainland Australia. This ferocious predator hunts a wide range of prey, ranging from insects to small rodents, as well as other marsupials, such as possums and the occasional wallaby. The Tasmanian devil also scavenges on the remains of dead animals, using its keen sense of smell to home in on the rotting carcass. Tasmanian devils have extremely sharp teeth and claws and their powerful jaws can crush through bones.

The quoll is another meat-eating marsupial that lives in Tasmania, Australia and Papua New Guinea. These predators are smaller than Tasmanian devils and eat a wide range of food, including plant matter, such as fruit and leaves.

Marsupials of the Americas

The only marsupials that live in South America are the tree-dwelling opossums. These small creatures are generally nocturnal and eat a range of food, from fruit and shoots to birds' eggs, chicks, grubs, small frogs and lizards. The Virginia opossum is the only species that has ventured north to the United States. The Virginia opossum has adapted to live in many different habitats and will eat almost anything it finds. One of the keys to the success of the Virginia opossum is its close association with human habitation. They shelter in outbuildings and scavenge human refuse for scraps of food. Virginia opossums have also been known to attack poultry farms and munch their way through garden crops.

▲ *The Tasmanian devil's famous yawn is misleading. The yawn is a display of fear and uncertainty as opposed to aggression.*

▶ *The Virginia opossum is the only North American marsupial. When threatened, this animal pretends to be dead to make the predator lose interest – giving rise to the phrase 'playing possum.'*

PIGS AND PECCARIES

Pigs and peccaries are hoofed mammals that feed on almost anything they can find. The pig family includes boars, hogs, domestic pigs and the vulnerable babirusa. Four peccaries belong to a separate, but closely related, family to pigs.

▶ *A female warthog stands guard over her four piglets. The warthog is a common sight on the African savanna.*

Members of the pig and peccary families share the same basic body shape, with barrel-shaped trunks, short legs, large heads and short necks. Most species have thin tails, which vary in size. One of the most distinctive features is the snout at the tip of the nose. The snout is a ring of cartilage, which is supported by a bone called the prenasal. Pigs have an extremely acute sense of smell and they hold the snout close to the ground when foraging for food. The snout is unique to the pig family.

The pig family

Members of the pig family live in large family groups, called sounders, which consist of females, called sows and their offspring. The males, or boars, usually live alone but join up with the sounders during the breeding season. Several males often fight for the right to mate with the females. The long canine teeth of the males grow up and out of the mouth to form tusks, which the males use as weapons when competing for mating rights. Boars also use the tusks to defend themselves from predators.

One of the most familiar members of the pig family is the long-legged warthog from central and southern Africa. These pigs live in mixed groups of up to 20 individuals and graze on the open savanna. Warthogs kneel down to graze and nip the tips off short grasses using their sharp incisors. In the dry season, when grass is less available, warthogs use their sensitive snouts to root out underground rhizomes. The babirusa lives in the rainforests of Southeast Asia. This large pig is threatened by human activities, such as logging, which is destroying the pig's natural habitat. Another familiar member of the pig family is the wild boar, which lives in the forests and grasslands of Europe and Asia. All domestic pig breeds descend from the ancestors of wild boars.

The peccary family

There are four species in the peccary family. All live in the forests of Central and South America and the southwestern United States. Peccaries live in large, mixed-sex sounders of various ages. They are closely related to pigs, but there are some key differences between the two families. For example, the canines of peccaries are much shorter than those of pigs and they point downwards instead of upwards. Peccaries also have only one lateral hoof on each rear foot (pigs have two), and their tails are also much shorter. Another key difference is the digestive system, which consists of three chambers and is more complex than that of a pig. The collared peccary and the white-lipped peccary are fairly common, but the tagua or Chacoan peccary from the dry shrubland (known locally as Chaco) of Argentina, Bolivia and Paraguay is on the brink of extinction thanks to overhunting. The fourth species, the giant peccary, was discovered in Brazil as recently as the year 2000.

◀ *A white-lipped peccary forages on the muddy forest floor, searching for plant tubers and small grubs.*

PRIMATES

Primates are some of the world's most familiar mammals. The group includes chimpanzees, gorillas, orangutans and many different types of monkeys, as well as less familiar species, such as lemurs and tarsiers. The primate group also includes our own species, *Homo sapiens*.

With the exception of people, who live on every continent on Earth, primates are restricted to tropical and subtropical regions. Most primates are found in the rainforests of Central and South America, in Africa and on the island of Madagascar (off the east coast of Africa) and in Southeast Asia.

Scientists once recognized around 180 primate species. In the past few decades, however, the classification of this diverse group of mammals has changed to encompass a wider range of species. As a result, zoologists now place around 400 species i n the primate order (group). The primate order and the species listed within it, has traditionally been divided into three main subgroups: the prosimians, or 'primitive primates,' the monkeys and the apes.

Shapes and sizes

Primates come in many shapes and sizes, ranging from the tiny pygmy mouse lemur, which weighs just over 40 g (1.4 oz) to the mighty mountain gorilla, which can attain a weight of 220 kg (485 lb). While there are many differences, this diverse group of mammals share certain body features. For example, most primates have nails instead of claws and they are all good climbers. Most species have muscular arms and legs and a powerful grip, which helps them hang on to the branches of trees. Some species have a prehensile tail, which acts as a fifth limb to hold on to the branches. Forward-facing eyes help primates judge distances accurately, so they can move between the treetops. Primates have bigger brains to judge the gaps between jumps. This increase in brain size means that primates are some of the most intelligent of all the mammals.

◀ *A pair of Japanese macaques grooming each other in a hot spring in Kogen National Park, Japan.*

▲ *A troop of ring-tailed lemurs walks down a dirt track in the forests of Madagascar. The lemurs use their distinctive banded tails as visual and scent signals.*

Feeding habits

Primates are a diverse group of mammals and they eat an equally diverse range of foods. As a general rule, larger primates, such as apes, mainly eat fruit and leaves and other plant material. Smaller primates have higher metabolic rates and cannot digest plant matter quickly enough to release the energy in it. As a result, small primates are more likely to eat small animals, such as insects and other invertebrates. Notable exceptions include the leaf-eating colobine monkeys. The stomachs of these primates contain bacteria that break down the tough cellulose that makes up the cell walls of plants. In other primates, a sac in the intestines, called the cecum, is full of bacteria that do the same job.

A few primates eat other vertebrates when the opportunity arises. Among them are the chimpanzees and bonobos, which chase prey, such as antelope and monkeys in raiding parties. The only completely carnivorous primates are the tarsiers.

Social structure

A few primates, such as the orangutan and some lemurs, lead solitary lifestyles, but most species are social animals that live in groups called troops. Some troops consist of several hundred individuals. Within each troop there may be smaller units, consisting of one male and a group of females or bachelor groups of juvenile males. Members of the troop maintain close bonds and help to keep the peace by grooming each other.

Primitive primates

The most primitive primates are the prosimians. Literally translated, prosimian means 'before monkeys/apes.' This subgroup includes lemurs, bush babies and lorises. Prosimians may be lower in the evolutionary chain than monkeys and apes, but they share the arboreal lifestyle and have grasping hands and feet to grip onto branches. Many prosimians are nocturnal

primates. Large eyes and doglike snouts provide them with heightened senses in the darkness.

Most lemurs are found on the island of Madagascar. These large primates have long limbs and long, bushy tails. Like all primates, lemurs spend a lot of time in the trees, but they also venture onto the ground where they bounce and hop on their hind legs as if they were dancing.

Bush babies are also known as galagos. These primates live in the rainforests of central Africa. Most species have long, bushy tails and have a distinctive childlike cry, which gives them their common name.

Lorises are the third group of prosimians and they live in India, Sri Lanka and Southeast Asia. These primates move hand over hand through the treetops, never losing grip of a branch.

Monkeys

Monkeys are divided into two main groups based on geography. New World monkeys, such as spider monkeys and marmosets, live in the tropical forests of Central and South America, from southern Mexico to Central America to Argentina. New World monkeys have prehensile tails, which provide them with another limb to grip onto branches. Old World species, such as baboons and mandrills, live in the rainforests of Africa and eastern Asia. Old World monkeys are more closely related to the apes.

Monkeys make up more than 60 per cent of all known primates. Different groups exhibit slightly different characteristics. Among the New World species, spider monkeys are lithe and athletic, howler monkeys are famous for their loud whoops and calls and capuchins and tamarins are some of the most agile species. The mandrill is perhaps the most striking Old World monkey, with its brightly colored face and rump, while the proboscis monkey is perhaps the most bizarre, with its long, pendulous nose. There are many other successful Old World monkeys and these include baboons, macaques and colobines.

▶ *The bright colors on the face of the male mandrill advertise his strength and dominance to females in the troop.*

The apes

Monkeys and apes are closely related, but there are some basic differences between the two groups. For example, monkeys have tails, but apes do not. Apes have long arms and use their hands like hooks as they swing between the treetops. This method of locomotion is called brachiation. Monkeys do not swing; rather, they jump from branch to branch.

There are two families of apes. Five species belong to the family of great apes. They are the orangutan, two species of gorillas, the chimpanzee and the bonobo

– a close relative of the chimpanzee. The lesser apes, or gibbons, comprise 15 species, all of which are found in the tropical rainforests of Southeast Asia. These primates can move incredibly quickly, swinging between the treetops at speeds of up to 56 km (35 mi) per hour.

Apes are our closest animal relations, so perhaps it is no surprise that they are also some of the most intelligent animals. Apes solve complex problems in a similar way to people and they have also learned to make and use simple tools. For example, chimpanzees commonly fashion small twigs into 'fishing rods' and use them to collect termites from their mounds. The chimp grips the twig between its thumb and forefinger and pokes it into the nest. As the termites bite hold of the twig, the chimp removes the stick and gobbles them up.

Gorillas are the largest of all primates. Both gorilla species live in the rainforests of central Africa. They are active during the day and feed on a wide range of plant matter, as well as the occasional termite. In fact, most of the gorilla's day is spent eating to sustain its great bulk. The dominant adult male (called a silverback thanks to the silvery hairs on its back) heads a group of up to 20 females and their offspring. These groups are very stable and females rarely leave a silverback, once they have paired up. Younger males also often stay in the family group.

With their brightly colored fur, orangutans are perhaps the most striking of all the apes. These primates live in the rainforests of Borneo and Sumatra in Southeast Asia. They spend most of their time in the treetops, picking off ripe fruit and other plant food. Orangutans are fussy eaters and will often peel fruit and strip plants before eating them. These primates also eat ants and termites, eggs, chicks and small vertebrates, such as lizards. Orangutans are unusual among apes because they lead solitary lifestyles. Males and females pair up to mate, but only the female looks after the young. The mother cares for her infant until it is ready to fend for itself, usually after eight years.

◀ *A female orangutan cradles her infant. The bond between the two lasts for up to eight years – for most of their lives, orangutans lead a solitary lifestyle.*

Primates at risk

Many primates are on the brink of extinction. The International Union for Conservation of Nature (IUCN) places more than one-third of all primates as either endangered, or vulnerable. One of the main threats to primates is loss of habitat as people cut down rainforests to clear the land for agriculture. Other primates are hunted for bushmeat, while some young primates are taken from the wild and sold as pets, or used in laboratories for medical research.

Tarsiers

One unusual group of primates, called tarsiers, share characteristics with both prosimians and monkeys. Tarsiers live in the rainforests of Southeast Asia, clinging to the branches of trees and scanning the forest floor for prey. One of the main features of tarsiers is their enormous eyes, which are bigger and heavier than their brains. Zoologists think that the ancestors of tarsiers form an evolutionary link between prosimians and simians (monkey and apes).

▼ *A silverback stands guard in the rainforest of Rwanda, protecting his troop of mountain gorillas.*

RABBITS AND RELATIVES

Rabbits and their relatives, the hares and pikas, are collectively known as the lagomorphs. These small herbivores live on land and occupy a wide range of habitats, from the Arctic tundra to the desert margins in Africa.

Rabbits, hares and pikas have a worldwide distribution, although there are few lagomorphs in the Caribbean (these have either been introduced, or are restricted to islands close to the mainland) and lagomorphs are notably absent from Madagascar off the eastern coast of Africa and from various Pacific islands. Lagomorphs form the main food source for many predators, including birds of prey, snakes and lizards and carnivorous mammals, such as the big cats. People also hunt rabbits and their relatives for sport and for the food and fur.

Body features

Rabbits and their relatives are often mistaken as the relatives of rodents, such as mice and squirrels. While both groups share many body features, such as similar body shapes and long incisors, there are several key differences. For example, rabbits and their relatives have lighter skulls and a second set of upper incisors – known as 'peg teeth.' Another feature that sets lagomorphs apart from rodents is their small, rounded tails. Unlike rodents, rabbits and their relatives also have fur on the feet, which aids grip when they are escaping from predators.

Many other body features have evolved to protect rabbits and their relatives from predators. Most lagomorphs have well-developed senses. Long ears capture the faintest of sounds, while many species have large eyes positioned on each side of the head, which provides excellent all round vision.

Rabbits and hares have long, muscular hind legs, which propel these mammals at speeds of up to 50 km (31 mi) an hour to escape the clutches of predators. The legs

◀ *A European rabbit feeds on a corn stalk. These small mammals are considered pests in many countries because of their legendary rate of reproduction.*

of pikas are all the same length so these lagomorphs cannot run as quickly as rabbits and hares. Instead, pikas are smaller and more rodent-like in appearance and adopt a different strategy to the rabbits and hares. They prefer to hide from their predators in underground burrows or rock crevices.

Feeding

Lagomorphs spend most of their time eating grass and other plant material. Plant food is difficult to digest, so rabbits and their relatives often eat their food twice. After the first passage through the body, these animals pass a pellet of partly digested plant material, which is eaten again. While this might seem disgusting to us, the process, called refection, is good for rabbits and their relatives because it provides them with the maximum amount of energy from their food.

Breeding

Rabbits and their relatives may be among the most hunted of all animals, but they are able to survive because of their high reproductive rate. Rabbits become sexually mature at a very young age – three months old in the case of the European rabbit – and the gestation period is generally very short. As a result, one female rabbit can produce six litters of up to 12 offspring every year. Hares are much less prolific and usually mate within a defined breeding season. For a long time it had been thought that hares seen 'boxing' was due to inter-male competition only. Closer observation has revealed that it is often a female hare 'boxing' with a male, either to show that she is not yet ready to mate, or as a test of his determination to mate with her.

▶ *'Boxing matches' between hares are common during the breeding season. Males fight for the right to mate with the females, while females clash with males if they are not ready to mate.*

RHINOS

There are five different rhinoceros species that live in different parts of the world. Two of them are found in the savannas of eastern and southern Africa, while three live in the forests and swampy grasslands of Central and Southeast Asia. The population of all five species is rapidly declining and three are on the brink of extinction.

The horns on the head of the rhino make this large, plant-eating animal one of the most distinctive of all mammals. Depending on the species, rhinos have one, or two horns. These fearsome-looking weapons are not extensions of the skull; rather, they are made up of a substance called keratin. Human hair and fingernails are made of exactly the same substance.

▼ *A black rhinoceros stands in the long grass of the African savanna. These bulky, muscular mammals are surprisingly speedy runners, reaching speeds of up to 50 km (31 miles) per hour.*

Body matters

All rhinos share the same basic body plan. These large hoofed mammals have short, stocky legs and heavily built bodies. Rhinos have thick, gray skin, which may be up to 2.5 cm (1 in) thick in places. In Asian rhinos, the skin is deeply folded so it that resembles plates of armor. Tiny lumps, called tubercles, look like rivets and add to the armor-plated effect.

The largest species, the white rhino, can reach up to 4 m (13 ft) in length and weigh in at more than 3,500 kg (7,716 lb). Despite their huge size, rhinos are remarkably speedy runners and can charge at speeds of up to 50 km (31 mi) per hour. Like horses and their relatives, rhinos are odd-toed ungulates (hoofed mammals). Each foot has three toes and there is one hoof on each toe.

Rhinos have very small eyes in relation to the size of their head and their eyesight is generally poor. Instead, rhinos rely on their keen sense of smell and acute hearing thanks to the large, rounded ear flaps, which channel sounds into the ears.

▲ Two male white rhinos clash in a battle for dominance. These fights often result in the death of one of the males.

Solitary or social

Most rhinos are solitary animals, but young adults sometimes form short-lived pairs and female white rhinos occasionally form small groups. Adult males are territorial. The territory of a single, strong male may overlap with those of several females and the male will mate if the female is receptive. Weaker males often share the territory of the dominant male, but they will be driven off if they attempt to mate with any of the females. Fights are brutal displays of strength and often end with fatalities. However, rhinos do not live up to their reputation as aggressive animals. In fact, they are fairly timid with people and will avoid confrontation if possible.

Rhinos at risk

Rhinos are some of the most endangered animals on the planet. The main reason is the demand for rhinoceros horn, which is an important part of traditional Chinese medicine (TCM). The International Union for Conservation of Nature (IUCN) lists both the Javan and Sumatran rhinos as critically endangered. There are thought to be fewer than 100 Javan rhinos left in the wild. The population of black rhinos is in rapid decline and the few remaining Indian rhinos are scattered over a wide range. The white rhino is the most numerous species. According to the IUCN, as of December 2007, around 17,400 white rhinos were estimated to be left in the wild.

RODENTS

Rodents are the most successful group of mammals, making up around 40 per cent of all the known species. These highly adaptable animals have exploited every type of habitat on every continent except Antarctica.

Zoologists have identified around 1,700 different rodent species. Despite the many differences in shape and size, all rodents share certain characteristics. Almost all species have compact bodies, with long tails and whiskers and clawed feet. Most species live on the land, scurrying around on all fours, while a few species make their home in the treetops. Some are burrowers and a few lead semi-aquatic lifestyles. All the members of this group are characterized by the large and continuously growing incisors, which rodents use to gnaw at their food. Indeed, the word 'rodent' comes from the Latin *rodere*, which means 'to gnaw.'

Sensing the world

Rodents are food for many different predators, so they rely on keen senses of smell and hearing to evade capture. As a result, most species have large, rounded ears and elongated snouts. Rodents also have acute eyesight, with large eyes set on either side of the head to provide good all-round vision. The final weapons in the rodent's armory of senses are the touch-sensitive whiskers, which provide an extrasensory dimension to the environment.

◄ *Rodents enjoy a love/hate relationship with people. Some keep rodents, such as these rats, as pets, while others regard them as pests.*

Feeding

Most rodents are herbivores that eat a wide range of plant matter, using their long, curved incisors to gnaw through hard food, such as nuts or seeds. The incisors grow throughout the rodent's life and are kept sharp by the constant gnawing – rodents eat continuously to sustain their high metabolism. Rodents also have a powerful bite thanks to their enlarged jaw muscle, or masseter.

Not all rodents eat plants. Some prey on invertebrates, such as insects and slugs and snails, while muskrats eat shellfish such as clams, as well as plant matter. A few rodents are scavengers and eat whatever they can find, including the remains of dead animals and human food supplies.

A rodent's digestive system is specially designed to break down the tough fibers in plant food. A sac, called the cecum, found at the junction between the small and large intestine contains bacteria that break up the tough cellulose, found in the cell walls of plants and convert it into sugars. Some rodents, such as capybaras

and guinea pigs, eat their food twice. After the first passage through the body, these animals pass a pellet of partly digested plant material, which is eaten again. This is called refection and helps these rodents derive as much nutrition as possible from their food.

Breeding

One of the keys to the rodents' success is their high reproductive rate. Small rodents usually reach sexual maturity after only a few months of age. Prolific breeders such as mice and voles may produce more than ten litters every year, and each litter may contain as many as 15 offspring. Since they are so numerous, small rodents form the staple diet of many predators but with little effect on the overall population. Large rodents produce fewer litters with fewer offspring in each litter. For example, the world's largest rodent, the capybara, produces only one litter of between one and eight offspring every year.

▶ *A female capybara nurses her litter of offspring. The capybara is the largest of all the rodent species.*

Social groups

Many rodents are highly sociable. For example, ground squirrels, such as prairie dogs live in a complex system of burrows, called 'towns,' which may stretch 600 m² (6,458 ft²) or more under the ground. Within the town, prairie dogs live in family units called coteries, which consist of one male, several females and their offspring. Coteries band together to form 'wards,' and all the different wards make up the town. Living in such an organized community provides protection from predators.

Rodent groups

Zoologists divide rodents into three main groups based on the arrangement of muscles in their jaws. They are the squirrel-like rodents, mouse-like rodents and cavy-like rodents.

As the name suggests, squirrel-like rodents include all the different species that resemble squirrels, such as the familiar beaver, prairie dogs and all the members of the squirrel family. While individual species differ in shape and size, most squirrel-like rodents have rounded body shapes, long whiskers and long, bushy tails. Beavers use their long incisors to gnaw on tree trunks and fell trees, which they use to build dams across rivers and construct homes, called lodges.

Mouse-like rodents include the familiar rats and mice, as well as gerbils, hamsters, lemmings and voles. This subgroup alone makes up nearly 25 per cent of all known mammals. Most mouse-like rodents have pointed faces, long whiskers and keen senses to detect the many predators that hunt them. The many species are highly adaptable and have spread across the world, exploiting many different habitats. Most species live on the land and emerge at night to feed on plant food such as seeds and shoots. Others, such as the muskrat, spend most of their time in water, feeding on aquatic vegetation and hunting for aquatic food, such as crayfish, frogs and small fish.

Cavy-like rodents include the world's biggest rodent, the capybara, all the other rodents that do not fit in to the other two groups, such as the spiny New World porcupines and African mole rats, as well as more familiar examples, such as chinchillas and guinea pigs.

▲ *A black-tailed prairie dog emerges from its burrow. These rodents live in a complex network of tunnels, called towns, which consist of several groups, or coteries, of prairie dogs.*

Most members of this group have large heads and stocky bodies, with short tails and slender legs. They are widespread in Africa, Asia and the Americas.

Pests or pets?

Many people think rodents are pests because they scavenge human food supplies and spread disease. Rodents eat millions of tons of human food every year, especially cereal grains and vegetables. They spread diseases such as Lassa fever and leptospirosis (Weil's disease) by contaminating our food and water supplies. People are locked in a constant battle with rodents, using traps and poisons to try and keep populations in check. Since they are such prolific breeders, however, these control measures have little overall effect on their survival.

Not all rodents are pests. Some are helpful to people by eating weeds and insects that damage important crops. Others, such as beavers, are farmed for their fur, while rats and mice are commonly used in laboratories for scientific research. And many people like to keep rodents as pets, such as mice and rats, gerbils and hamsters and chinchillas and guinea pigs.

SEALS, SEA LIONS AND WALRUS

Seals, sea lions and walrus belong to a group of mammals called pinnipeds. These animals have sleek, tubular bodies and strong flippers – adaptations that make them agile swimmers but very clumsy on land.

Pinnipeds are graceful swimmers and can twist and turn through the water at high speed. Some species can dive to depths of up to 150 m (492 ft) and can stay submerged for more than one hour. Pinnipeds spend most of their lives in the water, but they do come onto the land to breed and bask in the sun.

Body plan

The three main groups of pinnipeds share the same basic body plan. Most species have small heads, thick necks and flexible, tubelike bodies. A thick layer of blubber under the skin of pinnipeds insulates them from cold water, aids buoyancy and acts as an extra store of energy. Seals, sea lions and walrus have keen senses, with large eyes for good underwater vision and ears that can be shut off when they dive under the water. Most species have whiskers and these aid the sense of touch at close quarters. Inside the body, the skeleton has been modified to suit the pinniped's aquatic lifestyle. The backbone is extremely flexible, which allows the pinniped's body to undulate through the water as it swims. The short, strong bones in the forelimbs and hind limbs are modified to form powerful flippers, which can whip through the water and propel these animals at great speed.

Pinniped differences

There are a few differences between the three main groups of pinnipeds. For example, the flippers of the true seals, such as the common seal point backwards and they have no external ears. Sea lions and other eared seals have small ear openings and flippers that can rotate forwards, which means they can push their upper bodies up when they are on land. Walrus can also support their upper bodies. Male walrus have distinctive tusks, which set them apart from other pinnipeds. They use these elongated canine teeth as weapons during fights for mating rights.

◄ *A breeding colony of several thousand Cape fur seals bask on a beach at Cape Cross in Namibia. Males breed with a group, or harem, of up to ten females.*

Hot or cold?

Pinnipeds live in many different parts of the world, and they have to cope with a range of different water temperatures. Blubber insulates the body in cold water. In warm, tropical waters, pinnipeds flap their flippers to cool down. True seals and walrus can contract blood vessels near the skin to conserve heat in frozen waters. The can also dilate the blood vessels to warm up when basking on rocks.

Breeding

Seals, sea lions and walrus breed on the land. Males establish territories on beaches and other coastal habitats and they fight for the right to mate. Only the strongest males get to mate with females, which arrive after the males. Females settle in the territory of the strongest male and give birth to a single pup, which has been developing inside the female's body for many months. A few days after the birth, the female mates with the male, before they both head back out to sea.

▶ *The long tusks of the male walrus are elongated canine teeth. During the breeding season, the males use their tusks to spar with other males. The winner earns the right to mate with the females.*

WHALES AND DOLPHINS

◄ *A pair of bottlenose dolphins leaps from the crystal-clear waters off the coast of Honduras.*

With their hairless, streamlined bodies, powerful flippers and fluked tail fins, whales and dolphins may look like fish but, in fact, they are mammals. Most of the 84 species in this group are found in the world's oceans, but a few species have adapted to life in freshwater rivers.

Whales and dolphins form a group of highly specialized mammals, known as cetaceans. Like all mammals, cetaceans have warm blood and maintain their own body temperature. They breathe air into their lungs, rising to the surface of the water to blow waste gases out of the one, or two muscular nostrils, called blowholes, on top of their heads, before taking another breath. Like all mammals, whales and dolphins suckle their young with milk produced by mammary glands on the mother's body.

Adapted for swimming

All cetaceans have streamlined bodies to cut through the water with minimum drag. They also have a thick layer of blubber under the skin, which insulates the body from cool temperate and polar waters. The only body parts that stick out are the flippers and a dorsal fin, which aid stability and steering. The large fluked tail fin provides the main propulsive force. One swish of the tail can propel a breaching whale almost entirely out of the water.

A humpback whale opens *its vast mouth to reveal its long tongue and the sieve-like baleen plates on its upper jaw.*

Baleen whales

Cetaceans are divided into two groups: baleen whales and toothed whales. There are around 15 different kinds of baleen whales. Members of this group are filter feeders and trap krill and other marine invertebrates, as well as small fish, on hundreds of fringed baleen plates that hang from their upper jaws. Each baleen plate is lined with bristles that sieve the food from the water. Baleen whales usually have large heads to support the weight of all the baleen plates in their mouth. All baleen whales breathe through two blowholes on top of their heads.

Toothed whales

Most cetaceans are toothed whales. This diverse group includes all the dolphins and whales, such as the orca and the sperm whale. Toothed whales use their teeth to catch fish and slimy prey, such as squid. Unlike other mammals, which have different types of teeth, such as canines and molars, the teeth of a toothed whale are all small and round. Some dolphins have as many as 40 pairs of teeth on each jaw, while the beaked whales have just one pair of teeth in the lower jaw. The teeth are designed to last the whale a lifetime.

Toothed whales have large brains in relation to the size of their bodies, and they are known for their intelligence. The orca hunts in packs and may attack animals as large as other whales. It also snatches animals such as seals by 'surfing' the beach and sliding onto the land. Members of this group breathe through a single blowhole on top of their heads.

Sensing their surroundings

Most cetaceans have good vision in the murky ocean depths and can focus on objects up to 1 m (3.3 ft) away. However, many dolphins that live in rivers have extremely poor eyesight. River dolphins, like many other cetaceans, mainly rely on hearing to sense their surroundings. Toothed whales, such as dolphins, use a technique called echolocation, or biosonar, to 'see' with sound. They emit high-pitched clicks that bounce off objects in their path. The whales then detect the echoes and use them to build up an image of their surroundings.

Breeding

Most baleen whales breed during the winter. They migrate long distances from their summer feeding grounds in Arctic and Antarctic waters (where food is plentiful) to breed in tropical waters. As soon as they arrive, females give birth and then mate immediately. In the spring, whales and their offspring, called calves, make the long journey back to polar waters. The gray whale makes the longest migration of any mammal, traveling more than 20,000 km (12,500 mi) every year.

Life under the water

Cetaceans show some remarkable adaptations to life under the water. As mammals, whales need to breathe, but they can survive underwater for very long periods. Some whales dive down to great depths in search of prey. For example, sperm whales can descend to depths of 1,000 m (3,281 ft), or more in search of squid and can stay submerged for an hour and a half.

When diving, whales slow down their metabolism so they use up less oxygen. Some whales can slow their heart rate by more than a half. As they descend, the pressure of the surrounding water squeezes blood out of capillaries near the skin, providing more blood for the main organs. Water pressure also squeezes the lungs, forcing air back out into the windpipe. The respiratory tract secretes a foamy substance, which allows whales to absorb some of the oxygen in this air.

Social structure and communication

Many toothed whales live in groups called pods. Killer whale (orca) pods, for example, may consist of anywhere between six and 40 individuals. Since they live in the middle of the ocean, these animals are difficult to study and very little is known about their social structure. However, certain behaviors, such as cooperative hunting among orcas, suggest that the social structure is very complex. Baleen whales do not live in such tightly knit groups and rely on a complex language of clicks and calls to communicate with other members of their kind. Whales emit many different sounds, ranging from high-pitched squeals to low rumbles, which may have different meanings. These so-called whale songs are vital for communication between whales over vast ocean distances.

Cetaceans at risk

For centuries, people have hunted whales for their bones, meat and oily blubber. In recent years, however, intensive hunting with factory ships has devastated the populations of some species, such as the sperm whale. Many dolphins have also suffered thanks to intensive fishing methods such as trawling, since they become trapped in the fishing nets and drown. Laws have now been passed to protect these vulnerable marine mammals. Many countries now ban commercial whaling and the populations of many species are slowly starting to recover.

▼ *A bottlenose whale cow and her calf break the surface of the water to take a breath of air.*

WEASELS AND RELATIVES

Weasels and their relatives belong to a family of carnivores known as the mustelids. Members of this diverse family thrive in a wide range of habitats. Some species dig a maze of underground tunnels, while others live high in the treetops. Some species move between water and land, while others are aquatic mammals.

The mustelid family contains more species that any other group of carnivores. There are around 57 species, including badgers, ferrets, martens, mink, otters, polecats, skunks, stoats, weasels and wolverines. Mustelids have a wide distribution and are found across Africa, Europe, Asia and the Americas, but they are notably absent from Australasia.

Body features

With so many different species and such varied lifestyles, the mustelids do not conform to any general body plan. There are a few basic similarities among the members of this family, such as the short legs, the short ears and short snouts and long tails and long, curved claws. Another feature common to all mustelids is that each hind leg has five digits – most other carnivores have only four digits.

Mustelids with sleek, athletic bodies, such as weasels and martens, have flexible backbones. This enables them to twist and turn quickly as they chase after prey, such as rabbits and small rodents. Other mustelids, such as badgers, have more rounded bodies and tend to shuffle or waddle as they move.

Mustelids also have keen senses, particularly smell, which is needed to track prey. Smell is also important in mustelid communication, since these carnivores mark the boundaries of their territories with a pungent liquid secreted by glands near the anus.

Like most other mammals, the bodies of mustelids are covered with fur. The coat usually consists of a layer of short underfur, with longer, coarser guard hairs growing on top. The color of the fur varies according to the species, but it can be distinctive – as is the case with the black and white stripes of the skunk. This striking pattern acts as a warning for other animals to steer clear.

◀ *A short-tailed weasel has captured a mouse. To sustain its high metabolic rate, this voracious predator needs to eat up to one-third of its own body weight every day.*

Skunks spray a noxious liquid from their anal glands, which causes excruciating pain when it hits membranes such as those of the eyes and nasal passage.

Feeding and breeding

Mustelids eat a wide range of food. Weasels and stoats are lethal killing machines and can dispatch prey as big as rabbits. Some otters eat mainly fish, while others specialize in aquatic food, such as shellfish. The tree-dwelling martens hunt birds and squirrels, while ferrets hunt other burrowing animals, such as prairie dogs.

Mustelids are generally solitary animals, but males and females pair up to breed. Mating is often a rather long and drawn-out process. However, mating stimulates ovulation in the female so this virtually guarantees that the egg will be fertilized.

▶ *A giant river otter feasts on a fish. These semi-aquatic predators consume a wide range of food, including insects, crayfish, frogs, reptiles and the occasional vole or duckling.*

In many species, implantation of the fertilized egg is delayed until conditions become favorable for rearing the young.

Mustelids at risk

Many mustelids are hunted for their fur, which is highly prized and used to make coats and hats. The most valuable furs come from the mink and sable species. In the past, these animals used to be hunted, and the populations of many species rapidly declined. However, the American mink is now farmed for its fur to meet continued demand without destroying wild mink.

INDEX

NB: page numbers in italic indicate illustrations

PICTURE CREDITS

The publisher would like to thank FLPA - images of nature and their photographers for supplying all the pictures for this book.

Front Cover: Frans Lanting
Back Cover: Matthias Breiter/Minden Pictures, Scott Linstead/
Minden Pictures, Cyril Ruoso/Minden Pictures.

Front end paper: Frans Lanting
Back end paper: Richard Du Toit/Minden Pictures

Adri Hoogendijk/Minden Pictures: 117(b); Andrew Parkinson:
106(t), 124; Ariadne Van Zandbergen: 156–157, 158, 180; Bill
Baston: 139; Bjorn Van Lieshout/Minden Pictures: 22; Chris &
Tilde Stuart: 146, 147(t); Chris Mattison: 62–63, 65, 66–67, 69(t),
70, 71, 75, 76–77, 87, 92, 94, 95(t), 96–97; Chris Newbert/Minden
Pictures: 10, 46, 47; Chris Stenger/Minden Pictures: 155(t);
Christian Handl: 175, 197(t); Christian Hütter, I/IMAGEBROKER:
26; Cisca Castelijns/FN/Minden: 27; Cyril Ruoso/Minden Pictures:
12, 24, 68, 88, 137(b), 140–141, 202; David Hosking: 48, 117(b),
187; Derek Middleton: 49, 57, 86, 108–109, 191; Dickie Duckett:
105, 122–123; Dietmar Nill/Minden Pictures: 37(b); Donald
M. Jones/Minden Pictures: 147(b); Do Van Dijck/Minden
Pictures: 135(b); D P Wilson: 29; Egmont Strigl/Imagebroker:
59; Elliott Neep: 178; Erwin Van Laar/FN/Minden: 134; Fabio
Pupin: 78; Flip De Nooyer/FN/Minden: 100–101; Flip Nicklin/
Minden Pictures: 218, 219; FLPA: 93; Foto Natura Stock: 149,
174; Frans Lanting: 8–9, 39, 127, 161, 181; Fred Bavendam/
Minden Pictures: 17, 21, 44–45; Gerard Lacz: 50–51, 125, 151;
Gerry Ellis/Minden Pictures: 163(t), 196; Gianpiero Ferrari: 102;
Grzegorz Lesniewski/Minden Pictures: 171; Heidi & Hans-
Juergen Koch/Minden Pictures: 206; Hiroya Minakuchi/Minden
Pictures: 16; Hugh Lansdown: 11(t); ImageBroker: 53, 103,
120, 131, 163(b), 183, 210–211; Ingo Arndt/Minden Pictures:
144–145, 209; Jack Chapman: 30; Jan Van Arkel/FN/Minden:
28; Jan Vermeer/Minden Pictures: 118; Jasper Doest/Minden
Pictures: 116, 168–169; Jim Brandenburg/Minden Pictures: 95(b),
179; John Hawkins: 64(t), 137(t); Juan Carlos Munoz/Minden
Pictures: 164–165; Jurgen & Christine Sohns: 89, 107, 170, 203,
214; Kevin Schafer/Minden Pictures: 13; Konrad Wothe/Minden
Pictures: 197(b), 216–217, 220; Luciano Candisani/Minden

Pictures: 173; Malcolm Schuyl: 36, 90–91, 112, 198; Marijn Heuts/
Minden Pictures: 136; Mark Moffett/Minden Pictures: 25(b);
Mark Newman: 159; Martin B Withers: 167(b); Matthias Breiter/
Minden Pictures: 128, 152; Michael Gore:130; Michael Krabs/
IMAGEBROKER: 113, 213; Michael Rose: 30–31; Michiel Schaap/
Minden Pictures: 72–73; Michio Hoshino/Minden Pictures: 215;
Mike J Thomas: 20; Mike Parry/Minden Pictures: 52, 79(t), 82,
172; Mitsuaki Iwago/Minden Pictures: 143(b), 194–195; Mitsuhiko
Imamori/Minden Pictures: 34–35; Neil Bowman: 154; Nigel
Cattlin: 40–41; Norbert Wu/Minden Pictures: 56, 60, 61; Patricio
Robles Gil/Minden Pictures: 80–81; Paul Sawer: 106(b), 114(l),
167(t); Pete Oxford/Minden Pictures: 98, 110–111, 121, 155(b),
193; Peter Davey: 188–189; Peter Wilson: 25(t); Philip Perry:
114–115, 208; Phil McLean: 129; Piotr Naskrecki/Minden Pictures:
64(b), 69(b); Reinhard Dirscherl: 11(b), 14–15, 32, 32–33; Rene
Krekels/Minden Pictures: 74; Richard Becker: 23; Richard Du
Toit/Minden Pictures: 199; Ron Boardman, Life Science Image:
43; SA Team/FN/Minden: 221; S Charlie Brown: 153, 182; Scott
Leslie/Minden Pictures: 99; Scott Linstead/Minden Pictures: 104,
117(t); Shem Compion: 176–177; Shin Yoshino/Minden Pictures:
204; Simon Litten: 132; Stephen Belcher/Minden Pictures: 18–19,
200–201; Steve Trewhella: 38; Sunset: 115(r); Suzi Eszterhas/
Minden Pictures: 83, 142, 143(t), 189; Terry Whittaker: 119(t),
126, 133, 166, 206–207; Theo Allofs/Minden Pictures: 148;
Thomas Marent/Minden Pictures: 37(t), 205,212; Tim Fitzharris/
Minden Pictures: 138–139; Tom Vezo/Minden Pictures: 135(t);
Tui De Roy/Minden Pictures: 79(b), 192; Vincent Grafhorst/
Minden Pictures: 162; Wil Meinderts/FN/Minden: 42, 54–55, 58,
190; Winfried Wisniewski: 84–85; Yva Momatiuk & John Eastcott/
Minden Pictures: 184–185; ZSSD/Minden Pictures: 160, 186.

Every effort has been made to trace the ownership of copyrighted
material and to secure permission from copyright holders. In the
event of any question arising as to the use of any material, we will
be pleased to make any necessary corrections in future printings.

Project Managed by BlueRed Press Ltd